Born and raised in Manchester, England, now a proud Australian, Georgie Carroll is a comedian, author, nurse, wife and mother. This combination of nationalities, home life and hospital has provided a 24/7 training ground that has nurtured Georgie's naturally funny bones. Her bluntness and charm, coupled with razor-sharp wit, gives her a broad-spectrum appeal that sees her blow the roof off any comedy venue, anywhere.

Georgie has fine-tuned her talent to become the world-class comic, MC and writer she is now today. She has penned and performed five solo standup shows and appears regularly on Australian TV, including on *Have You Been Paying Attention?* and *The Project.* An excerpt from her first live TV special, *The Gloves Are Off,* called 'The Three Stages of Nursing' went viral, with 6.6 million views worldwide.

When not on tour, Georgie continues to nurse. Georgie has fused her comedic talent and love for her vocation in this, her first book.

# GEORGIE CARROLL

# OFF THE CHARTS

MACMILLAN
Pan Macmillan Australia

First published 2021 in Macmillan by Pan Macmillan Australia Pty Ltd
1 Market Street, Sydney, New South Wales, Australia, 2000

A catalogue record for this book is available from the National Library of Australia

Typeset in 12.75/19 pt Adobe Garamond Regular by Post Pre-press Group, Brisbane
Printed by IVE

Illustration on page 135 adapted from © Shutterstock.

MIX
Paper from responsible sources
FSC® C018183

The paper in this book is FSC® certified. FSC® promotes environmentally responsible, socially beneficial and economically viable management of the world's forests.

This book is dedicated to:

Artie Laing and Karen Laing at A-List Entertainment.
The wind beneath my stupid wings, for sure.

Cate Blake and Pan Macmillan. I have never had a
publisher before; I will always remember my first with
great fondness.

And Steve Carroll, my love. You are in the book as well
and I forgot to ask your permission. It is OK, right?
Love from the Wife xx

# CONTENTS

# ONE

# ADMISSIONS

## HELLO, WHAT HAS BROUGHT YOU HERE TODAY?

Hi, I am Georgie. I am going to be your nurse and a comedian for the next 275 pages. Forty-five years of living a fast and good life while not dying young have created me, a chaos embracer and balance denier who tries to milk almost every second for joy, cash, exposure or getting better at stuff. I present to you here, my latest endeavour to achieve all these things at once. It is a book, my first book, *Off the Charts*. It is a book of anecdotes and opinion pieces shaped from seeing the things you can only see over a life spent working in hospitals. The book may not be for everyone, so I have supplied a list of people who will be able to enjoy it. Check if you are on the list before proceeding as I am sure you are very busy, and I would not want to waste anybody's time. As I know all too well, time is precious.

## PEOPLE WHO WILL ENJOY THE BOOK IMMENSELY

1. New nurses about to enter the arena. Welcome. May the odds be ever in your favour.

2. Retired nurses. I know you are glad to be out of the scrum, but I know you miss the banter. This book has that, so let us reminisce.

3. Nurses currently balls-deep in the shit-fest that is healthcare. This book is definitely for you if you can find time to read it. If you love nursing, you will love the book. If at the moment you hate nursing, you will love the book more.

4. Finally, this book is for anyone who has ever needed a nurse, or fancies finding out what we talk about in the staffroom on night shifts. You are going to learn some stuff and laugh your arse off.

So, on reflection, forget what I said earlier. The book is for absolutely anyone. Enjoy.

Let me begin by telling you a bit about myself, where I come from, and introduce you to some of the players. The book tackles some big things so you need to trust me and know that I am real.

As you will discover, I am a born nurse but I qualified professionally in 2000. I have worked mostly in Intensive Care in the UK and Australia, but I now work in a less science-y and life-and-death hospital space that is much more suited. I now predominantly find lost slippers, which in itself does not sound exciting, but ooh, the thrill when you reunite them with their owners. So I do the slipper thing and I sing to elderly, confused people to stop them escaping from their beds after broken hips. I much prefer this to Intensive Care. I run this job in conjunction with a comedy career that sees me travelling the country to perform at festivals and comedy clubs. Sometimes I am not sure which job provides more fun. The disparity between the two careers is evident. One day I shall be doing something as purposeful as cleaning someone's dirty spectacles and feeding them porridge, the next I may be more celebrated as I describe the word cauliflower without saying the word cauliflower to a couple of dance mums from Gympie on the *Celebrity Name Game* TV show. It is a full life but not always entirely useful.

I live with my husband, Steve. I think he is an accountant of some sort, I am not sure. He has been in the same job forever and I do not really listen when he talks about the office he goes to. We have been together since '96, married in '01. We are the very best of friends with occasional benefits. He is my only ever significant partner and the only person I have ever romantically loved twice or sober.

We have two dependents: Rob, 14, and Tom, 16. They were raised, at least in part, by me, a nurse, so they are only dependent on paper. Both Steve and I believe ourselves to be as important as the children. When voiced publicly, this sentiment does not get received well in an era where the adults are supposed to centre their entire lives around the offspring. People often quantify their parental sacrifices by concluding that they would DIE for their children. For clarity, I would like to state that while we are as important as the children most of the time, Steve and I have discussed it and we would in fact die for them, but *only* if it came up as a dilemma. We would not do it just to prove a point.

For instance, if there were hostage situation, a home invader perhaps, who decides that what they need more than our limited valuables is to find out where Steve's and my parental moral compass truly sits. If it comes down to 'IT'S YOU OR THE CHILDREN', then we do indeed intend on making sure the children live on.

Steve would give himself up first. He is good like that and, as you will see in the book, very hard to kill. I would be up next. I have never had an actual fight but would give it a red-hot go rather than just surrender. With my dying breath, I would whisper, 'I love you, children. Do not let this senseless day of violence define you. It is not what happens to you, it is how you cope with it that counts.' Granted that is a long dying breath and the children don't often listen to me, so I might be better conserving the oxygen.

Steve's last words to the children would be 'Empty the dishwasher, the pair of you. I am sick of asking.' He may well ask the attacker to make sure to remember to take all their things when they go.

But it will all be for nothing as far as the home invader is concerned. They are screwed either way. Rob is a huge-hearted pacifist who struggles to lie, a rare and glorious quality in virtually any scenario, but absolutely obsolete in this one. Tom, however, is a fierce, brave defender who adamantly claims he could theoretically kill any living attacker with his bare hands if called upon to do so: rhinos, crocodiles and hypothetical home invaders included. This scenario is literally the only one in which I, his mother, would allow him to use his fists. I feel he would embrace it whole-heartedly, but should Tom be only able to talk the talk and not actually be capable of walking the walk, then Rob would definitely go to the police, describe the attacker perfectly and pursue justice through the proper channels.

I come from good stock. My maternal lineage has thrown out pendulous, seemingly cancer-proof tits, and vaginas that can take a beating in early adulthood but are prone to collapse on all sides if pressured by middle-age.

Both my mother and I drink ridiculous amounts of wine, enough to kill a person and even more when we are together. Mother drinks more than I but does not consider this a medical problem because the wine she drinks is expensive.

My mother's mother, Granny Whitworth, my first love, died while this book was being written. She died at 94 years of age. She died after just one hour of being in hospital for a cough. She died of being 94 and had a wonderful sense of humour right up until the last few moments. We know this because a UK nurse held her hand at the end and giggled at her stories, then phoned my mum and told her that. Hospital visitors were not, at the time, allowed.

If we look to our ancestors to see how we will age, I have a future where, unless I get home invaded, I will live to a ripe old age. Granny fell a lot but never smashed. She stayed on the floor and pressed her panic necklace so the ambulance crew could come and stand her upright again so she could carry on with her day. She kept her mental faculties and used them in part to help adult children clear the rooms of the recently deceased friends. She was more looting than helping. As a child of war and the Depression, she did not like waste. She would phone after a house clearing and tell me the spoils, 'I got a lovely porcelain mug and 12 toilet rolls. I don't know why he bought 12; he knew he was dying.'

On my dad's side, three generations of males have dropped dead of heart attacks in their fifties. However, my father, Keith (70), is a grim-reaper fugitive hiding in the mountains of southern Spain living an almost self-sufficient existence, mountain-bike riding and spontaneously marrying people so as to baffle the Angel of Death should she (it is definitely a woman) locate Dad in her next intake through town-hall documents.

Now you have met the people who built me and the people I built. It is time to start the book proper. Strap in, molls. Like any healthcare story, it is going to be quite the ride.

# TWO

# RECRUITMENT

## DO YOU HAVE THE X FACTOR?

A born nurse has finely honed emotional intelligence, an ability to handle both their own emotions and the capacity to handle others' emotions too. Along with ugly shoes and a poker face, a nurse will need to bring empathy, sympathy and compassion to work. If you do not know the difference between those three words, you probably are not an emotional black belt like I am. I can do all three, sometimes all at the same time. I can empath (feel your feelings) like a boss. I can compassion (relieve your suffering) you like you've never been compashed before. I will compassion you into the middle of next week if you let me. I would say sympathising (understanding why you are feeling like you do) is possibly my weakest skill but the force is still strong. In practice this means I can feel your emotional pain and I am driven to soothe it. But sometimes, if I am honest with myself, I do really question the validity of your emotions given the circumstances. Boiled down, I am a compassionate-guilty empath: I feel you; I judge you; I still care.

I am also upper-intermediate level at selflessness. I love a bit of belonging entirely to someone else for a while with no thought for myself. I might be doing it wrong, however, since apparently, I am not meant to get any feeling from it or just feel calm and centred or something. I never get nothing in return; I always end up liking myself more. I grab that feeling with both hands when it happens. It is not a calm feeling for me; it is a sparkling and energised lightness filled with endorphins and dopamine. It is highly addictive, and I love it. If true selflessness means I have to do work and not feel nice about it after, well you can keep it.

I know I sound like I like myself a lot, but I am as good as I say I am. Sounds narcissistic, a narcissist being someone with an inflated sense of self and a lack of empathy. I cannot be a narcissist because I like myself exactly the right amount, which just happens to be a lot. I also, let us all remember, have buckets of empathy; I am absolutely full of it.

All these qualities sound like excellent personality traits to have until you realise that for me to feel whole, some of you must suffer, and some of you have to suffer horribly. Do not think badly of me for it. Suffering is inevitable. I do not cause it, so it is a good thing they make people like me. The great thing about harvesting my self-esteem from human suffering is that it is never in short supply. Hospital is a wonderland for sort of selfless, occasionally sympathetic, compassionate empaths so it was no mistake that I ended up employed in one by the age of 21.

Claiming I am a born nurse is probably doing my mother and grandma out of some due praise. My triple-digit emotional IQ is a mixture of nature and nurture. The very reason I became a nurse was because Grandma said I could not be a pop star like I wanted to because I had chunky legs. She told me I was to be a nurse. Apparently, the hospital would not mind if I had thick thighs.

Mum's nurturing lessons were less direct and prag-matic than Grandma's. One of my earliest memories was our preschool trips to the Three Owls Bird Sanctuary, a rickety, midsized backyard passion project of a bloke called Kel. His only project. It was terribly named. For a start, it fell two and a half owls short of the promised three and provided little sanctuary for any of its birds. Kel was the proprietor and sole labourer at the shelter. He had built the whole thing himself out of whatever planks, pallets and grates he could salvage. All the enclosures looked poorly put together and the birds fared no better. Sparrows with Paddle Pop stick–splinted wings, pigeons wearing eye patches, one-legged balding chickens cradled in baby walkers. When I say there was half an owl, the whole owl was on display but wearing a head and neck brace. As an owl, if you cannot do the head-spinny thing, can you even really call yourself full owl? There was never anyone else there, so we always got the guided tour. He always knew a phenomenal amount about each of his birds including the troubling details of how they all got injured in the first place. Almost as if he had been present when each of the injuries occurred.

A 1912 medical book, *Backward and feeble-minded children*, used the terms 'idiot', 'imbecile' and 'moron' to grade delayed mental intelligence. Idiot meaning a mental age of less than two, whereas imbecile's brains were thought to have developed to that of only a seven-year-old. The moronic were considered to have a mental age of upward of seven but no more than 12. All these terms started as respectful labels before they were weaponised by the supposedly intelligent and 'normally' developed population, these feeble-minded types of people we now call idiots.

In 1912, Kel would have been a moron. In 1980, Mum carefully handed us the word 'retarded' to help us understand why Kel was different. The current 21st-century thinking, I believe, would be to leave out labels and to just call him Kel. Kel was not frail or ill in any way; physically he was hardy and calloused. He had a vulnerability, however, that came from being alone, lonely and lacking in some adult flaws and qualities.

I loved going to the sanctuary. It was not about the birds or Kel per se; it was about a feeling that the sanctuary visits gave me. It was a smaller version of what my mother was feeling. That lightness you get when you do something good for someone else while needing nothing in return. I have realised as an adult that the purpose of our family visits was not to look at the birds, in fact we had chickens and geese at home that I never bothered with. It was still about caring for all creatures great and small in some way. I do not know how they came into each other's world, but Mum took us there so that we could check in on Kel.

By the start of school, I was primed to care. Linda Frogan was my best friend in first and second grade. She would introduce herself to everyone by telling them she had epilepsy. Having epilepsy was something Linda really enjoyed about herself and it was one of my favourite things about her too. Linda had other great qualities: she was always up for making up dance routines and she had a killer scratch-and-sniff sticker collection, but our friendship was mostly built on the fact she could fit at any second and I would be there to rescue her.

She did not have a lot of epilepsy. She would fit at most once a term, just enough to keep things interesting but not so much that it was inconvenient to either of us.

She was a good learner case. Having a bit of epilepsy earned her some primary-school perks. For instance, she would say that she needed to sit on a chair instead of cross-legged on the lino during story time, and that I needed a chair, too, so she did not feel different. I, as a nurse, have had tertiary education regarding electrical activity in the brain, and there is absolutely no research to suggest that sitting on a chair and getting your friend an upgrade would be of any use as prophylaxis for seizures. I now realise that the chair stunt was a reminder to the class that Linda was special, lest we forget. Nice move, Linda.

Linda did not have the tremoring, frothing-at-the-mouth, biting-her-tongue seizures that people imagine. She just went vacant, like her brain had nipped off for a bit. She did slump off her chair. The teacher would have me sit next to her, with her in recovery position, until she came round and I could walk her to the sick room. Perhaps that is what the chair was for? If she had sat on the lino, there would be nothing to slip off. That was the sweet spot right there, the sick room. Post-seizure Linda and essential-worker me in the sick room. We did not call them fits or seizures; we would call it a 'tizwas'. I would ask her where she went when she had a tizwas. She would say she was not allowed to tell me; it was a secret. Six-year-old me was under the impression that this epilepsy was a magical superpower, not a disease, and I very much hoped to get it one day. The only true part of epilepsy that Linda could not put a spin on was that she would wet her pants when she tizwased. I saw it would upset her and little me would do wees in my pants, too, so that she did not feel bad about it. Peeing my pants was a very rudimentary way of showing solidarity with those in need. It did not follow into my adulthood, as it would make for a very messy shift and no work friends.

So far I was nailing selflessness, empathy and compassion. It was time to hone my sympathy skillz by over-shooting the target and helping in a way that weakens the person who needed help.

Johnny Irwen came to the school in Year 7, a withdrawn boy. His father had died. He did not tell us, and surely the teacher, Mr Carter, did not tell us, so we must have picked it up in parent schoolyard gossip. When the teacher asked for a volunteer to be Johnny's buddy, my hand shot up, it did it automatically for helper roles. Poor little lost, sad, semi-orphan Johnny, how could I resist? He was a fruitless mission; he never spoke unless spoken to and never gave any interaction of depth or joy. Almost as if the boy was grieving! We were not real buddies but as I had volunteered there was no getting out of doing pair work when it came up in class.

Being the fledgling empath slash compash that I was back then, I could not feel bright when I was around him. I was swamped by his grey and busy trying to lighten him up. I tired of him quickly and longed to be back with my more colourful friends. Mr Carter fed me some utter bullshit about honouring commitments when I tried to detach from buddying Johnny. Mr Carter had just had an assembly to commemorate his 25th year teaching at the school in which he had initially been a pupil. Commitment is not always a good thing, Mr Carter. I put this to him, and we struck a deal whereby Johnny and I only had to do pair-work activities together so that he did not feel completely abandoned. Mr Carter would bridge the gaps.

One such pair-work activity was the nature trail, a 60s classic that still holds value today. Children would wander into the woods two by two, one with a clip-board, one with a bag. The idea being to identify things in the forest – a pinecone, an oak leaf, a thistle – and pop them in the bag. I had given Johnny the clipboard, that way if he said nothing else, he would at least have to read the list out. My attention had been drawn towards a dead blackbird. I was poking it with a stick, rolling it over, checking for signs of life. Obviously after university, I progressed to more sophisticated methods but poking dead things to check for signs of life was pretty good improv for a 10-year-old with no medical monitoring equipment or training. It was a while before I noticed that Johnny was crying. He even sobbed silently! I am not sure what drove me to respond to his trauma in the way I did. I knew he was not a hugger or talker, so I . . .

. . . flashed him. I pulled up my T-shirt to my sternum and pulled my shorts and knickers down to just above my knees and showed him my front bum. He was surprised, not least because 'Georgie's fanny' was not listed on the clipboard, but I had no intention of putting it in the bag either. If I had asked if he would like to see it before I showed it, he would have shaken his head 'no', but people do not always know what is best for them, myself included. The crying stopped instantly, but there was still no talking. Johnny missed an opportunity there because seeing a fanny for the first time should have been a conversation starter.

I understand Johnny did not ask to see my fanny, and had we been older and had it been now there would have been a legal aspect and I would probably be on a register. Johnny did not take his eyes off it, however, and there were lots of other things he could have looked at had he chosen to. We were in the British countryside in spring. If you have never seen that, you should make time, as it's magnificent, but Johnny's eyes stayed trained.

Flashing at boys in the woods at 10 years old might seem a little young to some of you. I assure you in my hometown, Rochdale, it was age appropriate. It was the culture of our village. I had my first orgasm at the same age. It was spontaneous and unintentional. Surprisingly, it was in front of friends and family, which was not ideal, but I covered it by shouting out a food order at the point of twitching.

It was the summer holiday before Johnny joined the school, in Spain perhaps. We were holidaying with five or six other families, friends of my parents and all their children. One day, we were all in the pool when one of the parents asked what we all wanted for lunch. All the kids swam to the edge to give their order. Fate parked me right in front of one of those powerful submerged water jets that pump water in the pool. I reckon it took less than 10 seconds; I was pretty committed to it after the first couple of seconds though. I had no sexual thoughts at all during the build-up. I just clung to the side of the pool as my brain went somewhere. (I have no idea where, but I've been chasing that dragon ever since.) My eyes rolled into the back of my head and I shouted, 'HAM SANDWICH.' I floated for the rest of the day. I honestly wondered if I had just had a 'tiswas'. *Bloody hell, Linda, you kept that one to yourself*, I thought.

I never got out of the pool that holiday and tried to sneak a tiswas in as often as possible. I remember Mum and Dad bragging to their friends, 'She just loves swimming. We can't get her out of that pool. She is exhausted at the end of the day.' I am a lot older now, and it is a lot harder to orgasm. Sometimes it can take up to 30 minutes. I must think of things now, to be frank. My imagination must be a carousel of filth. Sometimes, even with all that, I do not reach climax. Mainly because the lifeguards tell me to stop. Apparently it is not in the spirit of aqua aerobics.

# THREE

# THE UNION

UNITED WE STAND, DIVIDED WE FALL.
ALL FOR ONE AND ONE FOR ALL.

A nurse starts their career with a truckload of compassion. Over the years, that compassion does truck off somewhere. This is what it can sound like.

I was on the morning shift taking over from a graduate nurse just finishing his first seven-night run in his first year of nursing. He had re-sprayed his deodorant and brushed his hair and his teeth for handover. I have been on dates with my husband where he has not put in that much effort. He read his handover from a script, so he did not miss a thing.

'Bed 7 is Peter; he is a 37-year-old gentleman with a six-year history of frequent admissions to hospital with ulcerative colitis, anxiety and depression. He presented to the Emergency department last night with abdominal

pain and sepsis. He was rushed to theatre; he had a perfo-
rated bowel. They have done a massive resection and they
had to give him a colostomy. He had a settled night on
morphine sub cut. Every admission, his biggest anxiety
has been that he would need a colostomy. He does not
know about it yet, but the surgeons will be around in the
morning to tell him.'

The mornings team leader had not turned up, so I got
moved to that role, meaning I got handover again. This
time from the night-time shift leader, Liz, a nurse who
had been on permanent nights for over 30 years.

Liz's permanent nights contract had been issued to her
in 1983 on account of being a single parent with school-
aged children. Liz was the last house standing; all her
night-nurse colleagues' contracts had been demolished.
Management had for years tried to oust her from her
nights. Their argument being that if they let Liz work
only at night, then everybody would want to. Never had
management been less in touch with what staff were
wanting.

It was a lose-lose bout for management and a complete
waste of energy on both sides. If they succeed in the fight
to pull her from the dark side, Liz would be working the
same hours as them, speaking in their meetings, meddling
with the policies, barking at consultants. This was a fight
management did not want to win. Even the dimmest of
farmhands knows you do not put the fox and the chooks

in the same cage. Let the fox skulk around in the dark while all the hens are safely tucked in the barn.

Like many night staff, she was frozen in the year she last lived in daylight. Liz had matted hair, the face of a Toby jug and the frame of a toffee apple. If working in a hospital teaches you nothing else, it teaches you that a person's outward appearance is no indication as to their usefulness. She was absolutely the nurse you needed around when a patient deteriorated at night with only skeleton staff to revive them.

Anyway, the handover. She had not brushed her teeth or hair for handover, or perhaps for many years. She was in the middle of her seven-night run three-quarters of the way through a 48-year roster. Imagine if you will, this handover delivered with Liz's broad Liverpuddlian accent.

'Bed 7, Peter. You know Peter, scabby bowel, a right soft cock. Anyway, came in last night and you will never guess what? His bowel has finally burst, surprise, surprise? Anyway, if they had chopped a couple of miles of it out and chucked it in the bin like they should have done two years ago then they wouldn't have had to move his arsehole to his abdomen like that. He's never been that taken with the idea of a stoma and he didn't know about it pre-op, so we've not told him, kept him asleep with morphine. Surgeons will be round in the morning to tell him.'

Liz is indeed a lyrical gangster; she stuck a little cherry on the top. 'Pffff, surgeons will be around in the mornin'?

29

But I'll give him my arsehole if we see them before teatime.'

None are immune to these character modulations; it is a necessary hardening. Even I, the cheeriest of all the nurses, have had to adapt.

In my early days, I would cry and remain solemn for the rest of the shift every time I laid someone out after death. I could not keep that up; it got on the other nurses' nerves and solemn does not suit me. I stopped the tears, but I still wanted to honour the recently dead in some way so after family and friends had visited, I would open a window so their soul could fly out. There came a point where I could no longer even do that as the hospitals had decided to glue windows shut, because people would throw their bodies out before their souls were ready. I have adapted to the hospital culture and practice of not chattering away about trite things during the washing, combing and shrouding. It still feels significant for the most part. I admit, however, that if I feel that someone had no one, or that I had a special connection with them, I will leave an open bottle in the room for the soul to hop into before the body is transported to the morgue, and then take the bottle outside so the soul can go wherever it needs to. Please do the same for me should I die in your care, just in case the afterlife is a thing.

Nursing changes a person, and the transformation does not happen overnight. It is a maturing and a ripening that happens over many years and can be broken down into three stages.

## STAGE ONE: STUDENTS OR GRADUATES THROUGH TO SEVEN YEARS OF PRACTICE

I call this crew the dolphins. The thing about dolphins is no one ever sees one and leaves miserable. Dolphins also have a level of devotion to humans that verges on Munchausen. They hang out in pods and are playful and squeaky. Although dolphins do not do any real rescuing, in a crisis they are excellent at flippering off to squeak at someone who can help.

A lack of experience at this stage is compensated for with overpreparedness. They don tool belts that hold pens of every colour, tape, personal thermometers, mini CT scanners and a couple of donor kidneys in case a patient requires a transplant. They turn up early for earlies, like early was not early enough for them, and proceed to fill out the cheat sheet with little boxes to tick after each job, assorted colours for different tasks, because crossing stuff off is sometimes just not enough.

Dolphins cannot survive on land so they carry ginormous water bottles everywhere, two litres, three litres, five litres. Little do they know that this water will be their downfall. They have not yet realised that real nurses do not take piss breaks. Dolphins will have beautiful skin, but they will prolapse.

Doing the morning weigh-ins of the patients with water retention (a routine morning task to track how much water the body is holding), dolphins are unhindered by the horror that will go with this task later in life. The horror that they have become heavier than many of the waterlogged even at their own dry weight.

## STAGE TWO: SEVEN TO THIRTY YEARS OF NURSING

I call this section of our tribe the penguins. Penguins can be sighted waddling in and out of the carpark at dawn, midday and dusk. They are still beautiful, but from a distance. If you look closely, they are missing bits, an eye, a tit. They are gnarled from the harsh environment. There are thousands of them, millions maybe, and if one of them is wounded or widowed the stronger penguins protect them in the middle of a huddle; everyone takes a turn in the middle at some point. The penguins on the peripheries peck at each other without doing any real harm for the most part.

The effort required for survival in the harsh health-care environment is relentless. As with the South Pole night and day, the hospital's daylight working hours do not run the same as the rest of the planet. Depending on the roster and the extracurricular schedule, the penguin could live in daytime or night-time 24/7 for months on end. Hardy creatures, they expect a lot from themselves, often supporting three generations of their own stock while also serving the needs of the whole colony. The penguin years are arduous and only in hindsight will a penguin see how large the workload and sacrifices were. In the moment they have no time to consider such things. When time allows, penguins sure know how to cut loose, skating and sliding around the ice on their bellies, usually on a drinks package.

## STAGE THREE: THIRTY-PLUS YEARS

These highly intelligent, powerful and majestic beasts are called the orcas. The swagger of an orca is not as spritely as the dolphin nor as hectic as the penguin. Instead they glide and have a bulk of self-assuredness about them that means they keep ploughing on regardless of how rough the sea is. Orcas in nursing, as in nature, are not even whales; they are, in fact, the largest in size of the dolphin family. They are fiercely protective of all humans; they shield swimmers from shark attacks. There are even many stories of killer whales rescuing drowning whalers, the very people sent to kill them. This is something that is embodied by the human nurse orcas, some of whom nurse and protect for 40 years or more. Neither type of orca would kill a human even for food. They are, however, the only mammal that has been regularly recorded as attacking dolphins.

# FOUR

## THE CHANGING ROOMS

### YOU GOT TO ROLL WITH IT.

The Rochdale Royal Infirmary was a small outlier hospital servicing the large and troubled population of Rochdale. To the rest of the UK, Rochdale is known for benefit 'fraud', tower blocks, racial tensions and civil unrest. It was often used as a casting pool for any production company making a documentary that asks, 'How shit is Britain?' For me, it was the place I lived for 34 years and where I clocked up my first decade of nursing (2000–2010). I was raised on the Intensive Care Unit by a tight group of staff who taught me to deal with teamwork, grief, marriage, criticism, self-doubt, ethics, conflict, forgiveness, motherhood and leadership while tending to Rochdale's sickest.

Change is inevitable in healthcare systems. Sometimes it is the needs of nation or advances in technology that drive the change, but most of the time, it is a newly appointed chief exec flexing their frugal muscle to a health minister who appointed them under a campaign. The campaign will always have a lame title like 'People Matter' or some similar beige nod to all the skull-fuckery being somehow about the community they serve.

Chief execs are the link between healthcare facilities and health ministers, so as you can imagine, the selection process is a business one stacked in favour of whoever is in power at the time. A much fairer way would be to vet applicants in a *Dragons' Den* consisting of the givers and receivers of healthcare.

### *Dragons' Den:* EP30000000000000

**Narrator:** Meet Erol Flunkton. He has spent the last 12 years building up the nation's largest online pet fashion business. Let's see if he can woo the Dragons with his plan to make healthcare profitable. Erol will be asking for 10 times the panel's wages in return for charging them for uniforms, increasing parking costs and implementing a computerised system that will make most of the orcas want to beach themselves. He intends to increase revenue by amalgamating and compacting services far away from the poor, popping a Nando's concession in the cafeteria and renaming the hospitals 'centres of excellence'. Let's see what the Dragons make of Erol's new 'Enriching Healthcare' model.

*Cut to shot of Erol tied to a rack getting rotten vegetables thrown at him while being disembowelled by the Dragons.*

It was 2010 when my beloved dolphin sanctuary imploded under such a campaign. Lots of services were to be pulled from Rochdale: Emergency, ICU, Maternity, so nothing vital to the community but still! These units were always overfull, so it was not lack of demand and there was nothing wrong with the building itself. The word Royal in the title was a bit misleading but it was otherwise a solid and incredibly useful structure.

As the closing date approached, our team felt resigned and redundant, feelings that would be stirred up years later watching Woody and Buzz Lightyear slip into the landfill furnace. We compensated for the sombre atmosphere by reminiscing, hugging, bitching and being extra silly to boost morale. We had a day of turning all cares into Britney songs. Easier than you would think. 'Put your mask on your face, cuz you're going hypoxic.' 'Womaniser, womaniser, wash 'em with hand sanitiser.' 'Ventilator, ventilator, gonna pop you on it later.' 'I'm a slave for you' came up a lot. We would often challenge each other to answer the phones with the phrase, 'Intensive care. Cutting edge of modern medicine. Georgie speaking, no one nurses you harder.'

There were lots of very strong accents in the staff, so

some days we would all agree to only communicate in Scottish as none of us were. This is how it came to pass that it was Sally who picked up the phone and introduced herself in Scottish when the bomb threat came in.

Bombing was big in the early 2000s, what with the Twin Towers and the lesser-known shoe bomber, a British Al-Qaeda member who hopped on a Paris to Miami flight with the intention of detonating the plane and its innards with his explosive-packed sneakers. His plans were foiled when he was overpowered by passengers before he could light the shoe's fuse. Even the best-laid plans, eh! One passenger restrained him with a belt while another held his head in place by pulling his ponytail over the headrest. Two French doctors sedated him with things they found on board. You cannot help but wonder if one of the things the doctors found on board was a nurse to go and find the things they found on board. The failed bomber wrote that he had some regrets; they were mostly tactical. Even bombers need to reflect.

Back to Sally.

'Well heylooo there. Roachdeyel Royal Infirmery, sister Sally, how can we halp yooooos?' she said brightly. She listened a moment, then cradling the phone in her neck, she started flapping her arms in panic. She grabbed a pen from her hair and wrote 'BOMB' on a pad.

'Oh, so yer sayin there's a boomb? On the u-net?' she

said, still in Scottish. It is hard to stop once you have started.

The staff who could leave the bedside were at the nurses' station with Sally now. She was making 'what the hell do I do now?' gestures. Demaan grabbed the Emergency flip chart off the wall and ran back with it open to code purple and pointed at the bit that says keep them talking and the list of suggested questions.

Questions you are meant to ask:

Where is the threat exactly? Which building? Which level? What does it look like? What will make it explode? When will it explode? Did you place the bomb? Who are you? How can we contact you?

Sally went with the following, her Lancashire accent returning. 'All right then, OK, errrr, are you sure you got the right unit? Rochdale Infirmary ICU? I wouldn't bother, we are closing anyway. Are you OK? Are you safe? You're not going to blow yourself up, are you? Do you mind holding while we just work out what we do about this?'

The line went dead. We left it off the hook, which was to this point the only bit of protocol we had followed. We then called security and executive as was mandated, but not until we spent a good few minutes unpacking what had just happened. We went through all the stages flitting between gossiping, minimising, denying and uncontrollably laughing at how chatty Sally had been.

'Should have invited him over for a cuppa, Sal.'

'He'd be wondering where the Scottish bird went.'

We were preparing all the patients for transport, which is no small effort as you cannot just stick sedated patients in wheelchairs, when Clevely, one of the security staff, entered the unit with a crate. We thought he was here to disseminate the evacuation plan. He was in fact telling us that there was no evacuation plan. Exec had decided it was probably a hoax. They were proper ready for our unit to close, weren't they?

Us: 'But what if it isn't a hoax?'

Clevely: 'Here is the plan: no visitors are to enter the unit with shoes on. They must put them in this box.'

Us: 'Where are you going to take the box when the shoes are in it?'

Clevely: 'Just inside the door; you know someone will nick the shoes if we pop it in the corridor and we would be liable.'

We all stared at Clevely long and hard enough for him to realise how stupid the plan was.

Clevely: 'What! It's not my idea. I'm just doing what I am told.'

Sally: 'It's all right, Clevely, sounds a grand plan. So long as we only get a little bit bombed.'

We took it upon ourselves to shift all the patients around to theatre recovery and stayed there and waited for a bomb squad to give the all-clear. The call was traced back to a disgruntled and disturbed acquaintance of an ex-patient. This kind of thing does not happen so much now because anyone unhappy with treatment can go and troll the hospital on its Facebook page instead.

I wonder, if our team had not been disbanded, would my family be sitting pretty in Australia? The withdrawal of essential services in my neighbourhood was an unreasonable price to pay to motivate my tree change, but I think had my hand not been forced I would still be working there but bitter and full of wanderlust.

Impermanence is a universal truth. There are jobs you can pick without day-to-day uncertainty. There is a bloke at my local Target who says hello to people when they walk in and goodbye when they walk out. He seems to love it. Even he must cope with change though, just not in his working hours. If, however, you choose to be a nurse, you must accept that change is part of the whole. For me this became easier when I thought of the health system as a kind Godzilla. If you are that big, no matter how well-meaning you are, you will trample people and buildings occasionally. Now all I do is look for somewhere more enjoyable if I am getting squished. Godzilla is gigantic, but nursing is bigger. The power is mine.

# FIVE

# HUMAN RESOURCES

### SCRIBBLINGS ON WORKPLACE BULLYING.

It is often said that nurses eat their young. I implied it myself in the orcas-killing-dolphins section a while back. I certainly had my fair share of intimidating mentors coming through the ranks, but I am pleased to report that I don't believe I have ever been workplace bullied, as such. As a chubby ginger child living in the poshest house in the crappiest suburb, there was absolutely some childhood bullying. Perhaps that made me a tougher adult, admittedly it could have gone the other way but thank goodness it did not. Someone may have tried workplace bullying and I may not have noticed. Or perhaps I have moved around too much; it is hard to belittle someone relentlessly if they do not hang around for it. So in summary, while as an adult I am not aware that I have been bullied, that is not to say I haven't partaken in some light workplace bullying myself, but we shall get to that soon. First, however, a little story from my teenage years about not letting the bastards get you down.

Katie Bamber was my best friend in my teens and twenties. She was the hot one and I was the dickhead. Katie was as much of a dickhead as I was but no one noticed on account of how hot she was. I was also pretty cute but no one noticed, again on account of how stunning Katie was. I shall tell you a quick story that involves Katie, myself, a group of young ruffians and some missiles.

Katie and I were a sought-after friendship group in high school, and I used to set dares for those who wanted to hang with us. This is obviously a bit bullyish, but at the time we just believed it to be very funny. There was not a lot to do in Rochdale. For one of the dares, you might have to go speak to the blind man in the bus station with one breast poking out of your school shirt. I was not a complete villain. I used to do it too. I would show prospective friends how easy it was by talking to the blind man with both boobs out. I knew he wasn't actually blind. Turns out anyone can wear sunglasses and carry a stick if they wish to.

Katie and I loved mountain biking. The town of Rochdale, as I explained, is not in itself a beautiful place but it is surrounded by magnificent structures: aqueducts, viaducts, railways, mills and canals stitched through the leafy green hills, brimming with pastures of livestock mooing, clucking and baaing, all sectioned by centuries-old drystone walls. Damn those Victorians knew how to build. See what good things happen when you put a woman in charge?

The world had moved forward in many ways since Queen Victoria, and it had moved backwards in many others. The picture-perfect landscape was now somewhat compromised by enormous electricity pylons straddling fields, graffiti on the empty mills and, for absolutely no reason I can think of, abandoned shopping trolleys in the canals. The trolleys infuriated me. Who takes an empty trolley on a walk down a canal? I suppose there could have been shopping in the trolley, but why, halfway home, would you think, *I'm going to carry the bags the rest of the way and hoof the trolley into the canal.* Katie would love how mad I got about the trolleys and was patient when one was near enough to the surface and edge for me to fish it out. Katie had a phobia of pylons ever since a national power TV advert with walking pylons had given her nightmares as a toddler. If we had to walk directly next to one, I could only get her past by piggy-backing her, fast-paced with her eyes closed while she panic-swore. I would have to dump her on the grass at least 50 metres past the mast. I would then shout 'Cover me' and dash back for the bikes, while Katie kept her eyes trained on the pylon, finger-gun locked and loaded in case it should start to attack.

One day, just after we had nimbly outwitted a slumbering pylon, we set off again down the canal. Nearly home, Katie was streaking ahead of me. She had been carried and then served as cover so she had the reserves to cycle. I, on the other hand, was sweaty and a little out of puff after heroically protecting her from the national grid.

We were coming up along a group of boys of a similar age to us, late teens, early adult. They were sat on the bank eating a chippy tea from newspapers. The boys were townies, a subculture of 90s UK teens who paraded around in spiffy, branded clobber to do even the most mundane of tasks. Even sitting on a canal bank eating pie and chips from newspaper required Burberry caps and Cabrini puffer jackets.

In my town, it was impossible to pass a group of townies as a female, a Pakistani, a limper, a ginger person or anything but a townie, really, and not receive an unsolicited approval rating of your physical manifestation. It was ingrained in everyday life and wormed its way into your psyche. More than reasonable, for sure, why not have lost boys allocate where everyone but them fits in to society? If the reviews were of a woman, they would be concluded with a 'would' or 'wouldn't'.

Katie glided past them first and was given a golden buzzer by all the judges, the audience went wild, whistles, applause, shouts of 'bang tidy' and a unanimous 'WOULD'.

I was next up for perusal. I did not so much glide towards them as huff, puff and grunt. The boys were at first silent, which sounds respectful but was somehow more horrific than insults. I kept my eyes fixed on Katie ahead and prayed for them to say something, anything. No words for me. I was indescribable, not even a 'WOULDN'T, NOT EVEN WITH SOMEONE ELSE'S'.

Instead I felt something fat, hot and slimy hit my arm, then another, then again. I was getting chippied. I say 'chippied' like it's a common thing in Rochdale, but it is not. I have never heard of it before or since, but chippied I got. First came the gravy-covered chips, then came the pie. A boy with bleached tips missed a direct hit, instead landing it on the ground in front of my wheel, the pie innards splattering up me as the wheel ploughed through. The rest of the gang seemed to need no further encouragement and chips smeared in curry sauce and gravy were lobbed at me, a cheer going up each time one landed on me, the target. They did not say they 'wouldn't' explicitly, but I got the general impression that I might not be worth a shag that particular day.

Katie stopped up ahead when she heard the commotion. By the time I got to her, I was crying, blotchy and splattered in curry sauce. Katie, furious, shouted, 'Cover me!' as she pelted back to give them a mouthful. It was like a dream come true for them, as some of them needed a good mothering and she served it to them proper. There was no remorse shown, so Katie cycled back, shouting, 'Fuck off, you unbrainy dicklings! Maggot dicks.' Which the townie boys loved.

I said, 'Leave it, Katie, they aren't worth it.'

Katie, not satisfied that she had taught them anything, simply said, 'I am not finished yet. I am going to hit them where it hurts.' We trundled back to Katie's in silence.

Once at home Katie set her plan in motion. She got a super-soaker blaster out of the shed, went to her pencil case, and began to squeeze all the innards of her fountainpen ink cartridges into the water pistol's ammunitions flask and then topped it up with water. I think you know where this is going and it is going to be just as glorious as you imagine.

Katie was about to do a drive-by shooting, and I was to be the getaway driver. I drove along the country road parallel to the canal till we found them, and Katie wound the window down and super-soaker ink-blasted their Burberry and their Cabrini. It was glorious; oh, how quickly the 'mighty' crumbled.

'All right, all right. Sorry the chips were only meant to be for a laugh! Stop! This is fucking Burberry. My mum's gonna kill me. All right, all right! It was only a joke, fucking hell, stop! We get it, sorry! Can you not take a joke?!'

We ceased fire and the boys scuttled down the canal track to get home quick smart to scrub the ink off their skin and ruined clothes. If the upside of being in a gang is that it gives you the arrogance to throw chips at chubby girls while they exercise, the downside would be that you all come off the canal at the chip-shop exit only to find that the hot girl you 'would' is now driving and the also-hot girl you 'wouldn't' now has the weapon of mass destruction and is lying in wait to give you one last blast.

Every large workplace contains some miserable characters of note. Their misery and snarkiness is usually overlooked because they can often be very efficient workers. Their attitude and bullying will have been taken to HR many times and the general outcome of mediation is usually that the rest of the staff must just get used to it. If you work somewhere with a large workforce, it will take you just seconds to list the top-three cantankerous colleagues. If you do not know who they are, beware. You may just be one of them.

In one UK hospital where I worked, one of the crabbiest staff who would fall into everyone's top three was a midwife on the Special Care Baby Unit (SCBU). She was called Sunshine. Such an incongruous name and workplace for a grump. I have never worked there exclusively but the hospital had a policy that nursing staff would rotate through SCBU to soothe the babies who were withdrawing from substances. Where possible, no staff member was to care for the Neonatal Abstinence Syndrome (NAS) babies on consecutive days. It is heartbreaking. If I remember correctly, the midwives would administer reducing doses of caffeine but the bulk of the relieving nurse's work was to hug the tortured newborn if their parents were unavailable. Swaddle their tiny bodies, pat their little bottoms, shush and sing them lullabies. I think in my whole career I have never felt more a nurse than hugging those beautiful, terrified bubs.

These shifts were draining enough without having a grizzly witch of a midwife shouting 'Put it down; it's not a toy' and 'Will you shut that baby up' from the comfort of her specially made ergonomic chair behind the midwives' station. There is always a shortage of chairs at a station but this midwife had one just for her that no one else was allowed to sit on. If I had a chair that fun, I would let everyone have a crack. It was like a saddle with arm and back rests. It had a 'Sunshine's Chair ONLY' laminated sign on the back. Work had paid for the chair because it was required for a back injury she had sustained at work. How in God's name you get a workplace back injury when your work requires you to lift nothing heavier than a prem baby, I do not know.

I'd had words with Sunshine herself and also complained to her line manager to no avail and was pretty much told, that's just Sunshine being Sunshine, get used to it. I could do that quite happily so long as Sunshine would have to get used to me. Because of the back injury, or perhaps because her name was Sunshine, Sunshine was not required to work night shifts, but I still had to. On nights, I would take great joy in sneaking down to that SCBU to fuck about with the settings on the saddle chair, heightening an arm rest, inclining the backrest, making the whole thing taller. I was just being Georgie. Sunshine struggled to get used to it; if anything, she became more of a bitch. Especially when she accused me of fiddling with her chair and I looked insulted and suggested perhaps it was the babies what did it. I never got caught despite Sunshine going to security and asking them to review the cameras from recent night shifts. Security had me covered, and said they saw nothing on the tapes, even though I know for a fact they saw my chair-tampering. They cannot have missed it. I had both my tits out when I did it.

# SIX

# HEALTH EDUCATION

'THOSE WHO CAN, DO, THOSE WHO
CAN'T, TEACH.'
- GEORGE BERNARD SHAW

All right, all right, everyone to the mats. Stretch your arms out to check that you each have enough space. Feet spread out, shoulder width apart. Ready? It is time to get healthy. Strap in bitches, I am about to embrace my inner-nurse/health educator/motivator so pop your sweat bands and spandex on and prepare to be given all the information you need for optimum health performance. OK, let's start. Jogging on the spot, keep those knees loose. Repeat after me:

1, 2, 3, 4
Tis better to prevent than cure. (I can't hear you!)
5, 6, 7, 8 (Nice and loud, c'mon!)
No time to procrastinate.

Right, that is quite enough jogging. Important not to push yourselves too hard the first few times. See you next week, but in the meantime, a little homework. Get yourself down the pool, people. No excuses. Even newborns can do it. You can just throw babies in a river and they will work it out. I very much question the ethics of the parent who discovered that. Also, do not try this at home. If you are an adult who cannot swim, what the hell have you been doing? Water is a third of the planet and with global warming, it is set to be more, get prepared. There is so much stuff we cannot do: fly, reverse park and invisibility. Swimming is a superpower we do have so get on it.

You can start off with walking in the pool. Traditionally, walking is a land-based activity, but the pool is a very accepting place. You may feel like a cretin and rightly so, but no one at the pool is thinking this of you. The water belongs to us all; use it how you like. There is a guy at my pool, a different type of guy, who loves the water. Burns all his NDIS (National Disability Insurance Scheme) coin on pool visits. He is never not there when you go. He either has a very good carer who stays invisible nearby until needed while pool guy lives his best life, or he has a very bad carer who dropped him at the pool one day and left him there, and pool man just made the best of a bad situation. He uses only a specific area of the pool. It is governed by which bits of him get wet and which bits stay dry. He likes to keep the tide around the floating ribs (the ones at the bottom) as he patrols his perimeter, hands out to the side, slapping the surface of the water so it dances. What I am saying is it is impossible not to find a way to enjoy the pool.

When walking in water gets boring, unless you like slapping the water at the same time, advance to land walking. It is something you do incidentally all the time; chasing toddlers, navigating pub crawls and escaping from Ikea. Unfortunately, though, for that very same activity of walking to have any cardiovascular or weight-loss benefits, it must be done in lycra and logged on social media. There is a small loophole: parking your car 15 minutes from your workplace and briskly walking the rest of the way will have unparalleled health benefits and you can do that in your work attire and not digitally brag about it. The eight-hour panic march while at your workplace will still not count, but the leisurely stroll back to the car will.

Back to the pool and aqua aerobics. This is the sweet spot of health and fitness. This is where all the cool people hang out: the pregnant, the land crippled and, predominantly, the seriously old. Some of the classes look like a casting call for *Cocoon: the musical*. Because of the demographic, the class area is at least one-eighth urine. In the chorus of Van Halen's 'Jump', it's possibly as much as a quarter ammonia. But do not let a fraction of wee stop you. As a nurse, I have been spat, shat, bled, vomited, phlegmed and weed at in a very undiluted, unchlorinated fashion and I am fine. I could probably scull a pint of that pool water and call it a lemon detox day. Perhaps even chew on the Band-Aids that float by for a protein boost.

The aqua aerobics instructor will razz you and the class up. I promise you, you will want to move. Who does not want to Macarena at nine in the morning, nipples deep in chlorine and other people's piss? The instructor can only do so much though. It is up to each person to push themselves to the limits of human endeavour. Aqua-aerobians need no SAS bootcamp sergeant wannabe yelling: 'Arms, Margaret, arms! Everyone else is walking like Egyptians! And you, you are eight beats behind still walking the bloody dinosaur! Wakey, wakey, Margaret. Stay back after class and I want 30 mins of flawless walk the dinosaur or you are out of the squad!'

There are dumbbells if you want to push yourself harder. They are fashioned out of polystyrene foam: the weights float! I understand the logic, there would be massive insurance implications if you gave out lead weights to the infirm in water, but giving people weights that float surely makes aqua aerobics easier. It is billed as suitable for any ability, but elite athletes could be quite snobby about it. Leave them sanding their areola away with cotton vests on ultra-marathons to get around the

Ozaki 8. We aqua aerobics mob may be pissing in a pool, but at least we are not poo joggers.

There are many other ways of exercising but I would not recommend them. They are fraught with danger. Sports injuries account for 3,000 dislocations, 9,000 soft-tissue injuries, 18,000 fractures and no one can even remember how many concussions annually. Yet in 20 years, I have never seen an aqua aerobics–related admission. It is in the shallow end so you would be hard pushed to drown, but if you were that inept in water, there are lifeguards around dreaming of being useful. They have been fantasising of this moment their whole careers, preparing by rescuing toddler turds out of the learner pool.

There are sports that pose no danger, but they have no discernible health benefits either. Some sports are so static you are almost at risk of clotting while performing them. Darts, snooker, pool, fishing, poker and luge to name but a few. But are they sports? Or did men in the 1800s label them as such so they felt less guilty about not washing up. Here is my rule: if it can be done wearing jeans and holding a beer, it is not making you fitter. If you are going to argue that they are sports, then I would also like to see tapestry, jigsaw and kitchen tea-towel fighting added to Fox Sports.

While luge *can* be done in jeans, it is hard to do so while drinking a beer without spilling it. It is still not a sport. I know it is not a sport because I did it and was excellent at it. If anything, being fatter makes you go faster and there is a lift to get you back to the top again. You cannot fuck this up. If luge is in the winter Olympics, then water slide should be in the summer Olympics.

It is worth finding a way of enjoying moving around a bit a few times a week, preferably in water with an 80s and 90s playlist on the speakers. If you do not enjoy aqua aerobics, go see a doctor. You may well be dead inside.

If all else fails, give water slapping a go. It did not rock my world, but it may rock yours. The plan is not to live longer; the plan is to enjoy the life you are living. With some activities, you may even die sooner than you would sitting on a sofa but you will have fun doing them. If you do end up living longer, remember that you spent that extra time doing aqua aerobics, so it was worth it.

Let us move on to diet. On matters of optimal nutrition, I am less qualified but still obligated by my profession to advise upon. I am more than happy to give it a crack if I have to but take my advice with a tablespoon of salt and a tub of Nutella. My teens through thirties were dominated by unsolicited diet advice surrounding weight loss, diet clubs, having a separate snack shelf to my brother, diet drinks and appetite suppressants. Much of the nutritional white noise of those years has since been proven to

be counterproductive and detrimental. I can only confi-
dently recommend whole foods and kimchi (fermented
cabbage). Nothing tastes better fermented. Traditionally,
the upside of the fermentation process is that alcohol is
produced, and kimchi does not even have this perk. It is
a dish that hipsters have hijacked from the Koreans and
crowned it as their own. It is cabbage but shitter.

The way to tell if something is a whole food or not
is to make it into a paste in a blender and then chew
it a lot before you swallow and digest. If it comes out
of your other end whole, it is indeed a whole food. The
way it works is by using the body's natural energy to put
the chickpeas and sunflower seeds back together on your
inside, making them minus calories. Whereas something like a Toblerone, once eaten, turns into a smooth
sausagey Bristol number four, letting your body keep all
its calories. Good job, too, no one would like to crap out
a whole Toblerone.

As you can see, putting me in charge of your nutritional health is as safe and useful as putting Ivan Milat in
charge of your Contiki tour. You can ask me for help but
I will redirect you to someone surer-footed, like your GP.
By GP, I mean Gwyneth Paltrow.

I am sure not to educate unless implicitly required to
do so. Should you be in immediate danger, should you
be writhing around on a gurney basking in strip lighting,
your gall bladder buckled yet again under the strain of

the forbidden fish and chips. Should you be shouting, 'Why is this happening to me?' washing away the regret with shots of pink ladies (medicinal drink containing antacids and lidocaine) and fentanyl. SHOTS, SHOTS, SHOTS! Once you are nice and pharmacy drunk, we can discuss why this is happening to you, and what to avoid if you can. It is the same thing as last time, we gave you a pamphlet with links to websites, it is still fish and chips. There is no judgement. I got hit by a car rushing across a road to the chippy. I scored myself some pretty villainous gravel rash all up one leg, but it was still worth it.

I am now and forever whatever weight I will be and I'm at peace with it. I am a glutton; I am greedy for all things (bar kimchi) including life. I am in it, I am on it, I am all over it and I am loving it. I am working on the frontline in a hospital in a pandemic, I am writing a book. I am raising a family. I am looking after my lover. You cannot do all that powered by a handful of chickpeas and some out-of-date cabbage. Aristotle declared gluttony a sin back in 300-ish BCE. Different times back then. Aristotle, quick word, mate: you cannot go around making broad statements like that in Ancient Greece and expect it to still hold water today. All you had was fish, figs and naked Olympics. You had no concept of all the delicious stuff yet to come. If gluttony is a sin, then let me be a sinner. Too much of anything delicious is not a sin and if you disagree, I will fight you. (It will be a food fight.)

I have not always had such conviction. I have been sat on toilet seats and hated on the thighs splashed out below me ready for judgement. I have grabbed at the fat and wished it would rip off like play dough. My hefty hips and roly-poly stomach have been stuck in clothes in changing rooms. I have protest-farted in stores that do not cater for plus sizes. My knees near collapsed under the weight of my bulk.

The shame of flab has led me to bariatric surgeons to discuss stomach staplings, bands, balloons and removals. None of these modifications extracts gluttony from a character so it was decided I could not be trusted around such delicate things. I have had countless splendiferous Sunday celebrations preceding martyrdom Mondays dribbling through to fuck-this Fridays. I have dedicated myself to longer temperances shedding 30 kilos of fat and dropping four whole personality sizes. I have had days in the past where I think of myself as only flabby and I say no more.

I have eight tabs open on my computer with recipes for Christmas lunch today and it is August. I am spooning a bowl of hummus, neat, into my face as a mid-snack snack. I look forward to meeting those chickpeas again tomorrow. I am a feeder and the fed. I am a plate/spatula/ bowl licker. I am a cheese-grater banger, bench-top hoover. I do not bring leftovers for lunch, for the love of Lizzo! If you have leftovers, it is because it was not worth eating the first time. If you do not have fairy bread at your kids' party, I am taking my kid home. You keep your five a day. I will stick with my 10. Yes, I eat after 8 pm. Why? Because calories do not wear watches. I believe that those who leave one bite of a sandwich on a plate are quitters. I would rather swig Coke and burp to fit more in than quit. I am gluttony! Hear me roar.

This body is mine. I built it. I live in it. I like it naked and I know how to dress it. It has studied hard. It has saved lives. It has made lives. It likes all foods. It is strong and independent. It hill-walks, cycles, swims, writes and makes people laugh. My body does not judge other bodies and is no longer critical of itself. My body has everything I need and does everything that I and others need it to do independently. My body knows that all these things are not always a given. So, if this body chooses to reward itself for being a legend by saying yes to all things including figs, fish and naked Olympics, then who am I to say no?

I could not fully educate you in the ways of illness prevention without talking about drugs, cigarettes and alcohol. There is no healthy level of cigarette smoking but it does look real mature and cool so I totes respect your choice if you do, bruh! There is plenty of comprehensive evidence to back up that it causes heart disease, shrinks a foetus, grows a cancer and destroys a lung. However, there is empirical/anecdotal evidence to suggest Great-great-uncle Brian chain-smoked from when he was in nappies right through to his 100th birthday, when he got hit by a bus while running a marathon. This fiction-fact obviously shits all over any of the medical science. I say this with the conviction only an ex-smoker can muster. Ex-smokers are the worst, right?

Time to get on to the drugs. They can be so many different things that it is difficult to give a blanket 'just say no' to. I said no to lots of them. I also enjoyed saying yes to a few. I have calibrated my opinion on them and came out the other end with stories, my family and a vivacious appetite for life.

Marijuana (THC) is commonly viewed as a mild, harmless drug. It is legal in many of the forward-thinking nations, and medically beneficial for physical pain and seizures. Obviously, you can become addicted, but you may lack the motivation to do so. Why would you bother? There is no pay-off as being high on pot is like having a pointless pyjama day, but slower: 'Me and Wozza were stoned right, and we started watching this YouTube video about sausage dogs doing bad parkour and we could not stop laughing. We laughed for like four days. Four days solid. We just had it on repeat.' If you need a mood enhancer to enjoy sausage dogs failing at parkour, it is time to get help or try something stronger.

Cocaine, when you are on it, makes you self-assured and unable to stop talking. I took it and had nowhere to go. It was given to me as a gift after the birth of my first child by a friend. She was electively childless and disappointed at how boring I had become in motherhood. She had a point. It took some nudging to get me snorting, I explained to my friend that I was worried it was addictive. She reassured me by explaining it was not addictive, information I trusted, she would know, she did it all the time. Having just done it the once, I feel that dabbling in it caused no long-term health risks, the biggest risk I had exposed myself to was snorting off the cistern of a pub toilet.

I have never injected. This is a waste given that I am incredibly good at finding veins. The injectables clearly have their upsides. The people who take them really love them, more than you love your grandma, but by the time these drugs are bringing them to hospital we, as staff, have totally missed the party bit. I have seen hundreds, maybe thousands, of people with IV drug-use (IVDU) issues and not one of them has looked to be enjoying it. Surely at some point they did. I have come to a conclusion. It is not an original thought, but it is one that I ascribe to. IVDU is not about the drug itself; it is about blocking past pain. Nobody exclusively takes class A IV drugs. If there is no ice readily available and they can only get their hands on oxy, or Valium, they do not refuse it. No one in a drug transaction ever said, 'No MDMA for me, I think I will leave it. I'm looking for ice. I am quite a bit of a purist when it comes to ice. Thanks, though.'

Opiates, hallucinogens, roofies, amphetamines and benzos. I am a sensation seeker and would truly love to try them all. Perhaps when I am in a nursing home? Perhaps one of each, frozen in unlabelled ice-cube trays. I could pop a random one in my sippy cup with my thickened fluids on a slow day. Have myself a little rave for one in the breakfast room. Till then, I shall numb my demons with the potentially just as damaging, but far more legal . . .

Alcohol, bars open! The healthy alcohol intake allowance for a female is . . . well, I do not know. If you do know, do not inbox me. Monday, Tuesday and Wednesday morning me would be very interested in that figure but it would ruin it for the mes of the rest of the week. I do know that the medical recommendations for women's alcohol intake are lower than for men. On a cellular level, alcohol hits women harder both at the point of impact and in the long run. Surely, at the point of alcohol impact, women should be allowed to drink more than men. Most women either counsel the fuck out of each other or dance better. Men on the other hand get a bit grabby or, worse, give long monologues about cricket and league and how to become an elite sports person despite me never wanting to be one and him never having been one.

+

Now we have taken care of the body, let us focus on the mind. Let us take the stress down a notch. Stop what you are doing. Give yourself permission to take some me time. Draw a warm relaxing bath and strip down, making friends with each part of your body as you reveal it. You are you; you are not the enemy; you are enough. Make sure you have locked the door. If you have young children, they may run in and ruin the calm by using your nipples as an intercom for a spaceship or something. Climb into the bath and take a few minutes to breathe and centre. Now it is time to start healing. First, imagine the person who created the stress is sat on a chair in front of you. What do they look like? Can you tell me what they are wearing? What do they feel like? What do they smell like? Then imagine you have another chair, a heavier, more solid one in your hands. Really feel it, its weight, its clumpiness. Now take that chair and batter the person in the other chair senselessly with it. Spend as long as you need on this section. Go until they have to crawl out the bathroom door with the only bit of them you have left whole and then drag them back in. Have another go at them if you need to. They will not fight back. They are imaginary – and you are naked.

Losing your shit occasionally is healthy. Never trust anyone whom you have never seen blow a gasket, and who denies ever doing so. Ted Bundy and Dr Harold

Shipman both presented as highly respectable pillars of the community before they were arrested for serial murdering. These previously esteemed and controlled men make excellent yardsticks to measure yourself by if you are having a bad day. Not just the men either. There was a mother at my children's primary school who claimed she had never told her children off. 'Don't believe in it,' she said. I saw her calmly negotiate a six-year-old through a 40-minute tantrum over whether it was munch crunch healthy snack time or not yet. Just give the kid the fricken raisins already. She claimed not to drink or smoke or medicate herself. She was a healthy weight and walked the children to school carrying their scooters in case they needed them no matter the weather. She said that if she felt a little frazzled, she would relax by doing adult colouring. There has never been a clearer sign of an adult not coping than doing colouring books. There is not a day that goes by when I do not want to call the police for a welfare check on her house. What freaky bucket for a toilet/human-centipede nonsense is happening to the kids under the house we do not see?

Is it just me or does anyone else actually enjoy stress? Not the tanty dance mums and the road-rage types, I mean the stress that feels like drive and focus. The pressure you feel when moving to a new house, or planning a wedding, or writing a book. It is a call to action, be it to pursue something good or to end something dreadful.

I can honestly state that I preferred being in labour to being pregnant both times. At least something was happening. Granted, when I have a lot on my plate, I am a high-functioning lush who grinds her teeth, does not sleep and I am quick to grizzle at my family. Yet if I do not have enough on, I am an underachieving, anxious drunk who entrenches herself in more of other people's problems than is healthy. In short, I am better served being overwhelmed than under. Yes, stress may cause strokes, high blood pressure and cancer but so does bacon and too little bacon is not good for a person either.

This brings me on to my last point. No matter how you handle your own affairs in diet, exercise and stress management, to avoid ill health you are absolutely going to want to back it up with large amounts of luck. No one knows who oversees distributing luck but we all suspect they are smoking crack when they do it. If Great-great-uncle Brian was in fact real, he was lucky right up until that bus hit him. Bad things happen to good people and good things happen to less-good people. Even with something as risk-free as aqua aerobics (yes, I am on about aqua aerobics again; it is my book and I will say what I want), there are no guarantees. There is a window where the unlucky may falter immediately after the class. The herd of octogenarians teeter across the slippery tiled Serengeti from the pool to the change room, their biscuity hips no match for the ceramic floor. Even with the best of healthy intentions, not all of them are going to make it.

# SEVEN

# STAFF HEALTH

### NOT NOW, PLEASE, I'M VERY BUSY.

Over the years if unchecked, a nurse is programmed to put themselves last. Holding their bladder to help someone empty theirs, forgetting their own broken heart to start someone else's, resigning from a unit you love to save yourself from a NILP (Nurse I'd like to punch) manager, missing a party to cover for a NILF colleague who needs the party more. What marvellous people nurses are, always doing for others till the list is finished. Therein lies the problem: the list is never finished.

Did you just say martyr much? Well yes, nursing is a religion of sorts. We talk about being led to nursing as a calling. We are a cult. The cult leader obviously being Florence. And we do indeed sacrifice and die because of our devotion to the movement.

Nursing has been a thing since people were a thing. Before Florence's revolution, the upper class got to go to hospitals while the lower classes were nursed at home. Many nurses were criminals avoiding prison sentences, the rest of the workforce were people too weak, old or too drunk to do anything else. Some shifts, it still feels like this is the rostering requirement. Miss Nightingale received the calling in the 1850s much to her parents' chagrin. She was meant to be marrying herself a nice boy and busying herself with being an accomplished wife: pianoforte, tapestry, fainting etc. Florence said yeah nah to the peaceful life and rocked up for a shift. She was a driven woman, by the sound of it. She introduced hygiene measures like washing stuff and in turn cut the death rate in military hospitals by two-thirds while up against typhoid, cholera and the Crimean War. She managed to write a book that revolutionised nursing too. Quite accomplished for a nonwife, right? I had a flick through the book. It is very wordy and I think mine's funnier, but no-nonsense Nightingale was a fly Mo' Flo' without a doubt.

I would like to take a second to ask you, the reader, to think of the nurses who have died in the line of duty through pandemics, plagues accidents, assaults and war. At the time of writing this book, more nurses had died fighting the Covid-19 pandemic than died fighting the First World War. Like all statistics this one is flawed; I think it just takes Allied Forces of the First World War into account. The Covid-19 numbers only account for 44 countries of the 199 nurse countries effected. Take some time to digest that, but come back cheery and ready to enjoy yourselves again please. This is a comedic book after all.

## THINKING SPACE 🔊

Thank you. Did you forget to remember the drunk, old, stupid ones from pre-Florence times too? Go back and do it properly this time please, children.

✚

A friend called me all distraught one morning, and I went around to her house to console her. She is not a nurse; she is an independent candle consultant. Independent candle consultant is a job, for reals. She helps people who struggle to pick candles on their own with their candle selection journeys. It is a bigger problem than you would imagine, people not being able to pick a candle. She holds candle parties (♪♪'There ain't no party like a candle party') because many people may need flammable scent of sea breeze salvation at the same time. The pragmatist in me feels that there would be less support needed if they made fewer candles. I have been to the parties, because . . . my friend. People at the parties have questions, can you believe it? Questions about candles. Sometimes I have questions because . . . tequila.

Where were we? Oh, yes. I got to my friend's to find her distress was down to a recent candle support therapy group having put in a massive order for Christmas and her finding out the order was not going to be in by Christmas. We put out fires and gained perspective over breakfast then she asked how my shift had gone. I was in uniform as I'd been on my way home from a night shift when she had called. It is hard to put across the pace and chaos of a busy unit to a friend who can give a 45-minute talk about wax and string twice a week and not bore herself dead. I said 'busy' and left it at that.

Had I not been desperate for my bed and second breakfast, I would have told her that when you get hand-over for a night shift, you make a list of things to do that night, and it looks manageable. You then add to that list the jobs that no one got around to in the day shift, then you add to that the list of things that have not been done since the hospital first opened. Then what happens is you introduce yourself to your flock and make sure they have buzzers so they can get your attention should they need you. It is the job of the flock to press the buzzers so you cannot blame them but it does mean the initial to-do list grows overnight, leaving the morning staff baffled as to what you did all night. The run of nights I had just emerged from was further complicated by a lovely old chap who did not press his buzzer once. The reason was not that nothing was wrong; he did not press the buzzer because the brawny, Polish, seventy-ish male's usually dependable brain had been temporarily turned to porridge by a UTI. His body was stronger and faster than a much younger man; he had a physique reminiscent of Roald Dahl's *BFG*. Until the infection cleared up, his brain was sludge at best. The urinary-tract part of his diagnosis meant he always felt he needed to pee even when he did not. The porridge brain meant he did not know he was in hospital. His stealth meant you were never quite sure where he was or if he would be dressed when you found him. He would usually be peeing on something you should not pee on; bins were a favourite.

*Delirium* secondary to UTI is a bread-and-butter presentation of any hospital so there was nothing too unusual about caring for this gentleman. Delirium is challenging enough to care for but BFG presented with a couple of challenges that made everything a bit extra. He was nocturnal. Unrousable in the day, in fact day staff handed him over as *moribund*, yet at night he could prance around like Fred Astaire. His other points of difference were that his much-needed hearing aids were never to be found in his ears, always in the sheets or in a jug, and that despite being a day-to-day English speaker, he had reverted to only barking loudly in Polish.

You work with what you have got; I even learned Polish

at one point. *Toaleta* is Polish for toilet. I had been saying 'toilet' for the past three nights following him around with a bottle while he weed on crash carts and other patients. The moment I said *toaleta* he took the bottle from me and ventured into the toilet. *Toaleta*, I left him alone in the bathroom and I gave myself a little pat on the back, believing I had cracked the code. *Toaleta*/toilet; I could see where the confusion occurred! I waited patiently, by the time I had remembered that there was another access door for the patients on the other side of the bathroom, he was again on the run, dribbling his balls around the unit. My colleagues and I eventually captured him and popped him back into bed, pouring his willy into the bottle and wedging it there with pillows. I sat with him, moisturising his knobbled papery hands until he settled, and then crept out of the room. I checked on him in the dark after a short while and the bottle was now on the night stand, I picked it up to find it was heavy enough to have had good use. The Pole was soundly asleep again.

I walked to the sluice contented that BFG's brain was at last putting itself back together. It was only in the strip lighting of the sluice did I see that there was no urine in the bottle. He had used it, but to defecate in. It is something I have only seen once. It was magnificent. It had not even touched the sides. The log had just landed stood up like the vegetables do in fancy restaurants. It was a perfect four on the Bristol stool chart, I mentally congratulated myself and the team for keeping him well hydrated. I would not have believed it was possible to shit in a urine bottle had I not witnessed it myself. Staff came from other wards to marvel at it and discuss the logistics. I am not sure I could do it but as soon as I get in an aged-care facility, I am giving it a red-hot go.

BFG was released home right as rain just a few days later with no knowledge or appreciation of his adventures in the last few nights. It had been unavoidable that he was in a share room with a lad in his early twenties whose mother had been reluctant to leave him alone overnight as it was his first hospitalisation. I think I had met her at one of the candle parties. He had come in for pinning and plating of a wrist. He went home with a much straighter arm but he was now an elective mute with new onset PTSD.

The shift work and chaos doth fuck with diet, stress levels and circadian rhythms. The ways in which the tiredness and stress show themselves are insomnia, over or under eating, drinking, smoking, drugs, withdrawal or anger. I have dabbled in all these things over the last 20 years, but my favourite self-sabotage weapons are without a doubt food and booze. The ways in which any of us reward ourselves for being excellent or compensate our failings is generally by doing something a GP would advise us to do less of or not at all.

I have not died in the line of duty, but I have had two full knee replacements. I am young for re-stumping, as 65ish is ballpark figure for your first renovation. There were three reasons behind the acceleration of my osteoarthritis.

1. **NURSING**: It is a very physical, on-your-feet-all-day kind of job. My knees would have lasted longer had I opted to sell candles.

2. **EHLERS-DANLOS SYNDROME**: I saw someone in a documentary have it and decided after rapidly paging Dr Google that I was also afflicted. I only carry one of the features, that of being very hyperflexible. I could just be double jointed but The Good Google Dr could not rule out Ehlers–Danlos and even suggested I may be part made up of Prader–Willi syndrome, just the bit of me that wants to eat everything.

3. **OBESITY**: I am, as mentioned, medically obese. Although this is factually correct, work does not accept it as a reason to phone in sick. I tried. 'Sorry I won't be in today, too fat to walk comfortably, I mean I could do half a shift but you might have to hoist me to the toilet on breaks.'

I first approached my GP 10 years prior to the knee replacement. I brought up the knee pain at an appointment about a sore throat. I was advised to lose weight to help the knees. I eat very well and I cook real food, but I am insanely greedy. I am never full. My GP explained the theory of needing to satiate the stomach, not fill it. She knew she was fighting an uphill battle because she had my notes and knew that greed was a chronic problem for me. It had nearly killed me once before.

In 2008 I had an Emergency-room presentation on anaphylaxis following a dinner of trout, green beans and jacket potato. It was a lovely meal that I had been looking forward to. A minute or so into eating the trout, I became swollen, cherry red and short of breath. All I could remember from my training was that it does not matter if you inhale a little bit of a nut or eat a whole nut, the reaction is the same. I took an antihistamine and finished my meal before presenting.

For the sore throat, the GP prescribed antibiotics and asked me to take them three times a day on an empty stomach. Given what we had just discussed, I could see some problems with administering this prescription properly.

You would think that devoting a life to tending people and the damage that their vices have done them would make a person behave. Instead when I see a two-pack-a-day 80-year-old who sculls 15 litres of goon per week, I think, *Oh good! I can do more goon.*

I am not the health educator best placed to advise

colleagues on self-care, that much is clear. If you are part of the workforce, how about this. Since we are so much better at caring for others, let us just do that. RUOK? is a great question for anyone who is angry or withdrawn at work. If it gets to a point where a colleague is drunk at work, however, it is imperative that you inform leadership so they can put the drunk person in charge of the hospital for the day.

# EIGHT

# SECURITY

QUEENSBURY RULES (3 MINUTES OF
FIGHTING FOLLOWED BY A REST).

At the hospital there is an open-door policy. Our door is open wide; we let anyone and everyone in. Some people like to come alone, others like a family day out. Once inside the open door, there is an extensive range of irritants to test everyone's metal. Waiting times, cancelled procedures, misinformation, hunger, pain, lack of sleep, lack of control and the brutal injustice of someone getting seen before you did. Anger can be valid; threats and violence, however, are not. A huge component of nursing is having the skills to douse angry spot fires to prevent the violent explosions. There are signs everywhere in hospitals to help people understand the culture.

VIOLENCE AND THREATENING BEHAVIOUR WILL NOT BE TOLERATED. PLEASE TREAT OUR STAFF WITH RESPECT.

The hospital has had the foresight to laminate the signs so that it is easier to wipe away the blood splatter after combat. If aware people are untameable and certainly if they are violent, charges should be pressed. There is however a violent community of patients who genuinely do not mean to be. To try to prosecute these patients would be as ridiculous as suing a baby for posseting on your shoulder when you wind it. Nurses are equipped with challenging annual behaviour-management modules. The modules encourage the staff to calm aggression by being understanding and giving compliments. It works up to a point, but by the time someone is throwing a desk at your head you have probably passed that point entirely. When they miss, complimenting them by saying 'Good arm' only tends to anger them further.

When I imply that some patients cannot help but be dangerous, your mind may have raced to people with schizophrenia or bipolar biting doctors' noses off while wearing the ward clerk's skin as a dress – knock it out of your skull. It is a convenient media-driven myth that having a mental-health problem makes someone violent towards others and it does make for great television. In reality, a person living with a mental-health diagnosis is far more vulnerable to assault and homicide than the rest of us. When those with a mental-health diagnosis do 'kick off' while admitted or detained, it is more often the system to blame than the patient. Luminous lighting, alarms and being watched 24/7 has notes of Guantanamo Bay to it, but it is also the vibe of the Emergency department for those in mental-health crisis.

If your mind has now moved on to drug and alcohol abuse, stay there for a little and calibrate your thoughts. I cannot unravel this one, not with any certainty anyway. I am uncompromising in my knowing that addiction is a disease as worthy of compassion and treatment as any other disease up to and including Bieber fever. I also know it to be true that consuming or withdrawing from drugs, alcohol and Bieber can turn a decent person into a selfish, unreasonable, wild, criminal, dangerous cunt. Where the disease ends and the person starts, I have yet to grasp. I have invited drugs and alcohol and Justin into my life at times. I have been a confidant, a gossip, a tower, a puddle, a ghost, a guzzler, a fox, a farter, a know-it-all, a drinks thief and a fibber. I have danced hard and counselled harder. I have thrown myself and others around hotel rooms in passion. I have woken up cringing and had to apologise after but never have I ever been a physical threat to others. (OK, maybe in one hotel room once, but we had a safety word.) So, when I talk about imbibed toxicity, I will leave you to make up your own minds about how much personable responsibility is applicable, if any. The consequences are devastating. The fallout lasts for generations.

Intrinsic toxicity, infection, brain diseases and injuries or lack of oxygen can make someone impulsive and risky to be around. Something as routine as high blood pressure generates adrenaline and a fight or flight response. These patients may well have no axe to grind and no processed intention of making you scared. They are, for all intents and purposes, unaware that they are out of control.

When deranged, the body has its own ways of poisoning the brain and therefore the nature of a person. Because these disorders are undisputedly iatrogenic (problems arising from a disease and its treatments), the fallout is our responsibility until, if ever, resolved. One such disease process is Hepatic Encephalopathy, which is a build-up of ammonia on the brain. It is one of my favourites. The head looks normal on the outside but the brain on the inside is that of an unruly toddler. It is a temporary, reversible condition related to liver cirrhosis most commonly, but absolutely not exclusively, associated with heavy drinkers. We get the piss off the brain through your arsehole, no joke, by giving ungodly amounts of enema to induce tsunami-like diarrhea, expelling the toxins. There is no reasoning with someone in Hepatic Encephalopathy. They have no idea that staff are people, so for many reasons we keep the Hepatic Encephalopothied chemically restrained (sedated). One of the reasons for this is that a nurse must, using only a keen eye and gravity, drip-feed gallons of a sugary syrup enema into the bowel of someone who does not realise they are a patient. The main reason, however, is that nobody wants to chase a bonkers un-toilet-trained adult with explosive diarrhea around a hospital, and if they do have to, how much do they really want to catch them?

We wake these patients up once a day for an hour. Now why would we do that given what we know so far? We do this because even when chemically restraining people, for everyone's benefit, we think primarily about how to do it safely for them. Also, the enema detox is not an exact science. How much someone loses their shit does not directly correlate to how lucid they become. We use a combination of testing ammonia levels in the blood and waking people up daily for an hour or so to see what percentage of them is planted back in reality.

Now, for the daily wakey wakey we do not just wing it; we are not idiots! You read the previous paragraph, right? We wear ugly non-slip shoes for a reason but even they could not handle this. We have shackles. That is right, we strap people's arms and legs to the bed frame. I am just going to let that roll around in your own un-piss-pickled brain before we carry on. It takes a bit, I know, to get used to the idea of tying people to a bed frame not being a punishment but being part of caring for them.

There is, of course, a 'strapping people down' policy. A doctor must deem it necessary and document it as an order. It is called a PRN or 'just in case' order, as in you use it if you run out of other options. Only three limbs are shackled at any one time leaving one limb whipping about like an unmanned power-washer hose. This is a chance to check the skin under the restraints and also a bit of accidental physiotherapy, so the muscles do not weaken for the final successful wake up. Exciting times indeed.

The first time I saw a patient in shackles it was because of Hepatic Encephalopathy. It was a perfect example of how these mechanical restraints work in practice and how doctors and nurses work together (or don't).

Mr Turps had been trying to rip all his venous and arterial drips and lines out and climb out of bed. Had the night nurse let him complete his mission, he would have bled to death before reaching the main entrance so as a safety precaution she strapped him to the bed. He was zonked by morning handover on account of him getting slugged with IV haloperidol after going six rounds with the night nurse who weighed less than his leg. The night nurse finished handover by asking not to be placed at that bed when he came back tonight. If ever there was a more telling sign of a shit shift!

Let me take you back to the year 2000. It is the start of my career; a time when doctors wore suits and ties; a time before electronic patient records; back when a super bug was something you might drive, and a gastric band was something you might jive to while courting.

**Scene: a hospital. The doctors are doing their rounds at 8 am.**

**Nurse:** 'Morning, doctors. Please do not wake this patient up. He has had a terrible night and has just gone to sleep.'

*The doctor wakes the patient by shaking patients shoulder vigorously and shouting at him.*

**Doctor:** 'Good morning, Mr Turps.'

**Mr Turps** (wide awake now): 'Evening to you, good doctor. You smell lovely today.'

*On the notes, the doctor puts a line through the order for the restraints and writes 'cease' across it and shows the nurse.*

**Nurse:** 'Maybe not just yet.' (She has spent more than four seconds at the bedside.)

**Doctor:** 'His ammonia levels are back to normal; he is reasonable. I would like him up and out and in a chair today please.'

*Doctor then flips his tie over his shoulder, whacks his stethoscope in his ears and goes in to listen to the chest. The doctor's tie falls onto the bed, and Mr Turps wraps the tie around his fist and cements it to his sternum. In a superb twist, the restrainer becomes the restrained.*

**Doctor** (futilely trying to prise Mr Turps' fingers apart): 'Could you let go, please, please let go, Mr Turps, let go now . . .'

**Mr Turps**: 'Fancy a snog?'

**Nurse**: 'Sounds reasonable enough. So would you like him in a chair or a bed for this kiss?'

*Grasping the back of the doctor's head, Mr Turps plants a smacker on the doctor's lips. Mr Turps is not about to bite the doctor's pretty face off; he just likes the smell of him. He does smell good. Mr Turps tries to grab the doctor again to pull him in for more of a sniff. It is quite an intimate moment for one of them at least; the nurse feels like she is intruding looking on.*

*Feeling like everyone at this point has learned a lesson, the nurse whips some dressing scissors out of her tool belt and cuts clean through the tie separating Mr Turps and his muse.*

***End scene.***

The restraint order was put back in place, but it was not needed again. He was indeed becoming more lucid and at this point his hands were content meddling and sniffing a third of the doctor's tie, and he was behaving on the promise of the other two-thirds. The moral of the story to any doctors reading is, if we say they just went to sleep, waking them up will result in you losing an item of clothing, and you do not often wear ties anymore.

We do not always have to deal with tension and aggression ourselves, we have security teams. We can summon them via panic buttons, ring them or at a push, nip outside to the smoking area and grab one. They have saved a nurse's bacon on many an occasion. They are not bouncers or thugs; they are not elite fighting machines either. If you were to face off with one in a one-on-one battle, you would think to yourself, *I can take them*. You only need to watch *Kung Fu Panda* though to know that you do not need a six pack to be an effective ninja; all you need is a bit of self-belief, some dumplings and a good team behind you. When security combine their powers,[1] they are unstoppable.[2]

Not all hospital patients require hospital treatments; some of them are simply living there while various agencies haggle over which will handle executive function and funding when they are released into the wild. We call these people the ward pets, the 'difficult discharges', or if the hospital is full, 'bed blockers'. The bed-blocker tag is an unkind one, it insinuates that the patient has a desire to block, but this is very much not the case. These people came to hospital because they were sick.

---

1   All the powers include pinning down, picking up, defusing, running towards, running away from, searching, detaining, expelling, lending cigarettes to and sitting on.

2   Not always; nothing's a given in security, bless their little cotton lapels.

We fixed what we could but could not fix everything or we made things worse, so the patients are lumped with permanent, complex-care needs too complicated for their pre-admission homes.

I have known this 'awaiting placement' process take up to a year or more for the ward pet. For the time they are suspended in this neutral zone, they are adopted by the staff on the ward. The domestic will chatter about a genuine shared love of dogs/Manchester United while dusting around the dogs/Manchester United clutter that inevitably personalises the room. The staff will throw in extra when putting in for pizza on night shift and make sure the ward pet gets plenty. If you are ever admitted, ward pets are easy to spot; they have their own proper mug and sit at the nurses' station. It is like business-class hospital to those looking on. They are wearing proper day clothes; this is said to make a person feel more like they are at home when we all know that home is where you take the clothes off and put the pyjamas on.

Grace was one of these ward pets. She was a former nurse who had developed Dissociative Identity Disorder (DID) aka multiple personality disorder. How perfect that such a diagnosis has an alias. Grace had four main personalities with a small ensemble of cameo characters. We liked all her personalities but some of them did not like each other which could make her selves unpredictable and violent, which we did not like. At her most difficult, her escalations were rapid and unbridled; she was a biter, a hair puller, a spitter, a thrower of punches, a thrower of anything, really. At her most playful, she loved balloon tennis, Elvis and *Shrek*. Because she turned any object to hand into a missile during conflict, her room had been multiple personalised into a grotto of soft toys. This made for many an entertaining code black; Grace would be in her room raging and swearing, pelting the fluffy contents of her room at a security team who would stand in the corridor doing Donkey impersonations and singing a medley of Elvis numbers till she either switched characters or ran out of teddy bear ammo.

I have in the past minimised, rationalised and engaged in the fallout of working in a profession with a zero tolerance towards violence and also a reasonable expectation of violence. I no longer do these things; I now internalise instead. It makes for vivid dreams, if nothing else. I had a truly awful dream after a tense day at the hospital just recently. I set the hospital on fire and then knocked out a firewoman with an extinguisher. While she was out cold I got her out of her clothes, put her in my scrubs and blamed the fire on her and everyone believed me. It was pretty mean of me, I suppose, so I probably deserved the nightmares. They have to build a new hospital now and she has promised never to do it again, says she cannot even remember doing it so they let her off with a warning. All turned out well in the end.

# NINE

# EMERGENCY

## IS IT REALLY THOUGH?

Before I was a nurse, I worked in an accounts office. 'Worked' would be perhaps the wrong word. I thrive on disorder and uncertainty; offices and junior-level accounting were scant on both of these elements. Very rarely do two and two not add up to four on a spread-sheet, although I could make it happen if I was really bored. I needed more. I would daydream constantly. If only we would receive an IRA bomb threat to relieve the excruciating boredom. Or better still, Phil Collins might barge past security and propose to me. Yes, agreed, Phil Collins is a bizarre fantasy for an 18-year-old or a woman of any age for that matter, but lust for him I did, and I now see it for what it was: a stark indicator of my self-esteem as a young woman in the wrong job.

The dread of working there forever in part drove me to seek out a life less ordinary, first by nurse training, and ultimately, by positioning myself in the Emergency department. There was no need to fantasise about work being more exciting anymore. I adored the pace, the growth, the purpose, the volatile natures. I loved that everything mattered.

Most of all, I loved the surprise goriness. I always had enjoyed my own flesh wounds. I was part cannibal as a child. I would pick the gravel rash scabs and place them in my front teeth to grizzle on. I would sunburn on purpose so I could peel myself. I would nibble at a wart while watching cartoons. I would spot a whitlow down the side of my fingernail at a sleepover and not sleep in anticipation of soaking it in boiling, salty, poultice water and sticking a pin in it to create a tiny hole through which to push out all the pus when I got home.

Now I got to view and mess with others' boils and barnacles. I saw some sights: degloved feet, amputated fingers in ice-packed freezer bags, butterflied penis, and I remember them all fondly.

As a rule, all substances and lumps causing discomfort, barring blood and some major organs, are better off out than in. If this part is making you retch, then perhaps you do not have the strong stomach required to nurse (not to imply I still eat the hospital offcuts). Many state that they would have loved to nurse but grow faint at the sight of blood. Let me assure you blood is the most elegant thing to spurt out of a human so if you don't get used to that you stand no chance with the other fluids. I love all the things a human can expel and if I had to rank the things that fall out of humans in order of beauty, I would go: blood, pus, babies, urine, parasitic worms, shit, prolapses, vomit, sputum and, finally, maggots.

I loved and still love the connection to people. The connection is sometimes more intimate and authentic than the bond I have with people I have known for years. There is an implicit trust that most medical staff inspire in people that means we can request things of a person that would not be acceptable from anyone else.

I think nothing of saying, within seconds of meeting a person, 'Could you please take off all your clothes, underwear, too, and pop on this gown? It's open at the back. Hop on the bed on your left side, curl up in a ball, and hug your knees to your chest. Someone is going to be in in a moment. I'm not sure who. They are going to pop some fingers in your bottom, and I am going to stand here and watch for legal reasons. Then I'm going to write in this file what the doctor did to you and that you agreed to it. Then about lunch time, I am going to stand at the end of your barouche with some of my friends and tell them what happened.'

You say that to someone in an Emergency department and they just do it. Try whispering that very same thing to a close friend in Kmart and see what reaction you get.

GEORGIE CARROLL

The Emergency department is like any team or army: you need leaders and learners, defenders and attackers. If you were to think of it in terms of *The Lord of the Rings*, you need the homely hobbits, unlikely looking heroes who often surprise themselves with what they are capable of.

You need the wizards, miserable but wise and old. They have seen all. They can produce actual magic, they bring things back to life with just their hands and minds, and more impressively, they can make a department fit for 50 patients house double that. They decide who shall and who shall not pass. Wizards are few and are used sparingly as they tire easily.

There are many, many elves. They are identical, immortal and spritely. Elves stay immaculate, even in battle. They are older than their outer appearance and have seen much more than others who look so youthful. Elves look fragile but are very difficult to kill. However, they may turn into orcs if tortured and mistreated.

Most importantly, there is a glut of dwarves, unglamorous, effective, lumps of pure endeavour and bravery. The dwarves are a hilarious, rough-and-ready bunch when on the well-worn path but become hardy, selfless defenders when friends are under attack. The team as a whole is greater than the sum of its parts and they work together to never finish a relentless journey brimming with purpose, fraught with obstacles and danger. Much like *The Lord of the Rings*, those subjected to the

108

Emergency department feel that the whole saga took 10 times longer than it needed to.

There will always be some waiting around when it comes to ED. Many are often surprised by that. There is a reason it is called a waiting room. No one knows the reason why the people in the waiting room are called patients. The waiting room is not devoid of entertainment; it may or may not have a TV screening a 'Right Here Today' type program on loop with a sensationalist, damning report on the nation's health service being at breaking point. No one can change the station over or off because it is bolted high on a wall so that disgruntled patrons cannot trash it. They can, however, steal the remote and they do.

If there is no telly, there is bountiful people-watching to do. Peak viewing would obviously be Friday and Saturday nights, but anything can happen at any time. There are cliffhangers and intrigue, and way more questions than answers in the personal stories you are attempting to piece together. Why is the woman who demanded a wheelchair from the carpark able to walk outside for cigarettes? How on earth does a person nail-gun themselves through the foot?

The long wait and the fascination with others can create the perfect conditions for two who consider themselves hopeless in love to find hope in each other for a while, usually in the disabled toilets, and self-discharge (in every way) before medical review. Emergency flings are more prevalent than you would imagine. The Ska chick in me thinks it must be love but the rapper in me is fully aware that it is more likely a tornado and a volcano just hooked up. The hopeless find hope in each other and for a while the tornado stays a spinning vortex, the volcano continues to bubble the magma it has been stockpiling since its creation. Isn't this a thrilling love affair? The cyclone may dislodge some rocks and blow some dust off the bulky structure making it feel new. In turn this makes the chaotic swirling feel like a Whirling Dervish on account of being useful and needed. If unmonitored, the volcano will erupt and shoot molten lava up into the vortex, knocking the wind out of the tornado and devastating the lives of anyone nearby.

There are no shortcuts to moving through the Emergency departments. How you arrive at ED means nothing to the triage nurse. Turning up in an ambulance does not score a patient business class. Assuming as much would be as ridiculous as arriving by horse wearing a fascinator and expecting to be transferred immediately to the Melbourne Cup. Triage nurses (T1) have tough calls to make and people see them as trolls, but they are not. They are dealing with several people's accidents and emergencies, not welcoming people to summer camp. I have worked in triage, but never as a T1. I have been a T2, a kind of waiting-room concierge. It is a cushy position.

T2 keeps an eye on you to check you do not get sicker, gets all the gossip and apologises for not knowing how much longer you will need to wait. The waiting room is basically no fun for anyone but the T2.

Waiting rooms (yes, we are still in the waiting room. I appreciate your patience. I honestly do not know how long it will be before you are through to the department proper) are undoubtedly more frustrating when someone else arrives after you and looks all right and gets whizzed through. As previously mentioned, I am never T1. I am not qualified to tell you how triage officially works, but from my time as T2 and my many times as a parent or patient in the waiting room, this is how I think this is how it works. If you get whizzed, the good news is no waiting, the bad news is you are on the verge of or over the edge of fucked. If you get moved through quickly, it is because you need screening and treating for something that could fuck you over shortly. If you seem to be there for ages and ages, you may feel the worst you have ever felt but you are stable. It is hard to believe at the time but there are still several levels of fucked you could achieve. Please be patient; this too shall pass. If you need to be there and find yourself getting testy, soothe yourself by remembering waiting around is fucked but being whizzed is fuckeder by a mile.

There is aggression and violence in the ED for all the reasons and excuses that we discussed in the Security chapter because some people do not know they need to come to hospital but they clearly do as they are a hazard to themselves or others. Paramedics or police (I do not know which) occasionally have to use nets to catch people safely out in the community. I think the official name is security blanket, but they are nets. I do not know how they get the people into the nets and the only way I can rationalise it is to imagine that the paramedics or police place something on the floor that the patient may want and then when they bend down for it, the net drops and the patient stands up all surprised and says, 'You got me proper this time, you pesky paramedics. Tsk. Off we go then.'

The net is removed once the patient is in hospital and there are other means of restraint. The one and only time I have seen the net it was getting removed in the resus room. It had been harbouring a woman we often saw in Emergency. She was reliably violent, aware of it and had been non-repentant to this point. She had had a very busy day prior to presenting this admission. She should have been exhausted. She wasn't.

A relationship breakdown in the morning triggered some grand theft auto. Nothing heals a heart quicker than stealing cars, am I right? A high-speed police chase ensued. The police won the race by default as our patient had landed her car in a river. South Australia is the driest state in the driest continent on the planet. Managing to find a lake big enough to drive a car into should be commended.

I was not officially part of the resus team; I was there to watch and learn. Nurse Roy was R3 (third member of the resuscitation team) scribing, so he was writing down what was happening in the resus as it happened. Roy is a staple of any ED.

So far he had written:

17:07 Patient in R1. Bought in by SAAS post RTA and near drowning. SAPOL in attendance. GCS 15, unable to obtain respiration rate as patient yelling obscenities. Oxygen levels 97%. Chest X-ray done. IV access x2 obtained. In police custody, combative. Safety blanket removed, shackles applied. Patient a known Hep C and spitting, face shield applied to patient.

Roy had a student with him. If Roy was a dwarf, solid and weathered, his student would be a budding elf, elegant and a little aloof. The student was clearly quite taken aback by the woman in the bed, distressed, soaking wet, shackled, in a net, spitting on herself in a mask. It does look a little bit 'burn the witch' if you do not understand why it was all happening. Once things were a little calmer and our downers had neutralised the patient's uppers, Roy asked his elf if she had any questions. The elf spoke some wisdom.

'How ethical is it to put a woman in a net like that?' Go, Elf!

Dwarf Roy: 'How else do you think we get people out of water?'

Elf: 'Really?'

Dwarf Roy: 'Yep, we are not allowed to harpoon them anymore.'

Those who spend a decade or more working in the Emergency fellowship can become desensitised and nonchalant to the threat of violence. Even with this patient strapped to a bed and under police guard, she posed a threat. On a previous admission, while shackled she had head-butted a security guard for stealing her cardigan, and she was wearing the allegedly stolen cardigan at the time!

Some staff keep frequent reoffenders in line with a 'Go on then, just you try it. You so much as look at me and my colleagues wrong and I will pop some benzos in your glute with the biggest blunt needle we have, got it?' That seems to work. I am not that brave. I am a hobbit more than anything else, not even a Frodo, more a Sam. I am skittish around violence and wish I could just disappear when it happens. I often do. I have to pretend a lot when around someone with an Alert (a documented history of hospital violence), like I think they can smell fear or something. I go super-efficient and just get through what needs to be done with a smile, making sure I am nearer the door than the patient is at all times.

Hopefully you never get to see inside a resus room and just move into a cubicle. A few things to note that will assist staff and make the whole journey run smoother for you. Firstly, emergencies and accidents usually involve some pain. You will be asked to score your pain out of 10. Please note 11 is not out of 10, and neither is 20. Pain is whatever a person says it is, however, your score will be halved if you are taking a selfie while describing agony.

Secondly, you will be asked if you have allergies. Saying, 'Yes, to antibiotics, but I'm not sure which one' is not helpful. It just makes the medication round feel like a game of Russian roulette. Being allergic to bee stings is perhaps irrelevant in hospital unless you came in as a result of your allergy, as we tend not to administer bee in hospital. Same goes for long-haired cats.

Thirdly, if your barouche gets turned around so your feet are at the wall and your head is at the curtain and someone comes in with a head torch and a chaperone, you are about to get an internal.

Fourthly, if you have had the same problem for days/months/years and have not sought medical attention until today, it may not be an emergency. We cannot tell you it is not, but check yourself.

Fifthly, if you are unlucky enough to get bitten by a venomous snake or tarantula, please bring a picture of the offending animal so we can identify it, not the actual animal. If you absolutely feel compelled to bring in the attacker, please be sure to tell staff what is in the bag before they rifle through it to check valuables.

Finally, after an eternity it is now time to leave the Emergency department. And try to remember on which fucking level you parked the car in the multi-storey. You may notice that 'fuck' is said quite a lot in this chapter. Eighteen times to be precise. Apologies for the strong language. The word fuck is the culture of the Emergencies and accidents. As with both the end of your Emergency encounter and the end of LOTR, you are often left none the wiser and with no more fucks to give.

# TEN

# INTENSIVE CARE

## NO ONE LOVES YOU HARDER.

Emergency and Intensive Care nurses are both nurses in the same way that Dobermans and Chihuahuas are both dogs, same species but very different breeds. In a primary-school assembly, the young Intensive Care nurse would be up at the front receiving the principal's award for organisation, whereas the Emergency nurse would have to sit next to the teacher after being caught writing 'fuck' on a rock with another rock.

If you were to invite both to a house party, the Intensive Care nurse would be tidying up downstairs while the Emergency nurse is upstairs pissing in your husband's aftershave because she caught him cheating. An Intensive Care nurse would prepare for coitus by douching for their partner, before laying a towel down to protect the

ironed Egyptian cotton sheets from the inevitable spill-
ages. They are not complete prudes; they would always
douche again and change the towel before the next shift
came on. An Emergency nurse would likely leave your
gown open at the back and tell you to shave yourself with
a rusty razor before a surprise pegging.

What is Intensive Care? In soap operas, Intensive Care
beds are reserved for when a hot person falls into a coma
for a couple of hours and the next of kin usually wrestle
with the idea of switching off the life-support machine
for 10 minutes or so before they turn it off at the socket.
If the soap character is popular enough with the public,
they wake up with amnesia in a wheelchair and then have
to learn to walk again while falling in love with the handsome physiotherapist. Absolutely nothing about this
scenario is credible.

Comas are sometimes 'fallen' into, but patients are
more commonly 'pushed' into a medically induced coma.
A combination of sedation, painkillers and occasionally paralysing agents are trickled into your larger veins
through a catheter that is inserted through the skin deep
into the vessels. This enables you to tolerate the breathing
tube. The intubation breathing tube goes in through your
mouth, down into your upper airways, so you understand now why we keep you asleep? Or if we need you
awake, we use a tracheostomy tube, which allows different
concentrations of oxygen to be pumped into you, and all

the differing types of sputum and mucus to be suctioned out of access in your neck. Although a tracheostomy will leave a scar, it does give you the ability to communicate by writing and using communication picture boards as only your voice box has been bypassed. As you are awake, it also allows you to add some of your own much-needed efforts to those of the medical and nursing team.

Your family do not get to choose to flick a switch, ending your life. Those decisions are way above the paygrade of the average person. The doctors will, however, take into consideration families' wishes and definitely prolong your life until all your loved ones' expectations are sufficiently managed. Your family does have work to do, though. They will fill your cell with pictures, rosary beads, healing crystals, Harry Potter scarves, worried stares and long bouts of silence interspersed with unanswerable questions.

There is no life-support machine. Instead there are endless machines, alarms, beeps and a nurse sat at the end of the bed, the orchestrator conducting all of the organs in your body by tweaking machinery to support the organs to maintain life, but not so much that they enable the organs to become lazy. It is as vast as a network of tubes and cables going deep into the largest vessels removing all your blood, cleaning it and replacing it. It is as insignificant as 1IU of insulin being delivered precisely over one hour. Finally, the physiotherapist certainly is handsome but probably not lovable.

The music for the nurse conductor is written by the intensivist team of doctors. They prescribe a complex score that changes several times a day. Every organ, gland, limb and cell has a part written for it. Although intensivists are perfectionists, they do not expect perfection from each of the body parts. They just ask that some of them at least try to play. If you can get just a couple of the organs going with gusto, the peer pressure often makes the rest of them join in.

The patients on Intensive Care are the sickest of the critically sick in your city. To work in Intensive Care, you must love detail and trust science, but more than anything you must believe in miracles.

My first exposure to Intensive Care was as a student, 20 years old and green. I spent every shift of my nine-week placement at Tchako's bedside. He was my case study assignment up until his 113th day on the unit. The essay this placement produced was my first piece of creative writing as I had to pretend that any of what we had done in nine weeks was in any way beneficial for him or me. I thought I would be cracking open chests and pumping hearts with my bare hands in the Intensive Care placement, not documenting hourly a spectacular lack of effort and progress.

All Intensive Care patients have one to one nursing. You cannot take your eyes off the bed lest an infusion stops or a tube blocks. You had to keep two sets of eyes on

Tchako because we had some pretty solid evidence that he held suicidal ideations and he had been there long enough to understand he just needed to remove his tracheostomy or turn up a couple of the drips to achieve his goals. The two pairs of eyes came in the form of myself and the Intensive Care nurse, Cynthia, who was supervising me. It was on day 113 that I, a second-year nursing student armed with one semester of 'how to do the counsellingy stuff' and absolutely no lived experience of black dogs or demons, saw what I believed to be an opportunity to make a real difference. To work my miracle.

The shift started much like all the others; every morning handover was an echo of the previous day. The ICU nurse and I, her student, started our shift.

Nurse Cynthia: 'Hi, Tchako. We are going to have a good day today. I will just get handover and I will be with you.'

Tchako chose to not respond, his glassy fish eyes looking at nothing at all.

Night Nurse: 'Tchako Vinn, 36-year-old chap. Failed suicide attempt by hanging. He is having a bit of a low day again. Bit weepy, aren't you, Tchako? Day 113 on ventilator through tracheostomy, slow wean but we are going to get there together, aren't we, Tchako?'

Handover complete.

Now let's break this down and discuss it. So few words, so much said.

+ **'Failed suicide attempt'.** A failed suicide attempt is now called a suicide attempt or nonfatal suicide, thank goodness. Why you would tell a suicidal person that they failed at something 113 long days on the trot I do not know.

+ **'Having a low day again and a bit weepy.'** Calling what Tchako was feeling 'a bit of a low day' was tantamount to saying the Pope is a little bit churchy.

Tchako had a lot of low days; 113 days straight that we had documented evidence of, and at least one diabolically low undocumented day before that.

I love a good cry myself. If I have a cry trapped on my insides that needs to come out, I watch *Father of the Bride*. This film is my mental-health barometer. If I cry at the opening credits or, worse still, do not cry at all, I get myself checked. I cannot fault Tchako for crying, which seems very valid if you got to the point where you wanted to feel nothing then landed in a place where you could not escape feeling everything.

He probably needed space and time to talk, to document for himself what led up to the diabolical day.

+ **A 'slow wean'.** Tchako was on a ventilator with a tracheostomy. As mentioned, the tracheostomy means we cannot take our eyes off you lest it falls or get pulled out. A slow wean is just quicker than saying, 'There is nothing wrong with his lungs that a little bit of effort would not fix but Tchako ran out of effort 114 days ago.' Breathing requires muscles: the diaphragm, the intercostals. Use them or lose them. They pack up quickly. Off the ventilator, Tchako put in no spontaneous breathing effort apart from the tiny amount of added inspiration he delivered accidentally by constant sobbing and sniffing. Not to worry though.

+ **'We will get there together, right?'** We have to; there is no choice. If you do still want to die, we cannot and will not let you. It is against everything we stand for if you have something we can fix. You need to get physically well and off ICU before you can make those decisions for yourself again. To get to that point, we need you to pull up your anti-embolic stockings, get some concrete down your feeding tube and harden up. We are going to need you to hop on board if we are ever going to get you out of here.

First job of the morning was the bed bath. The ICU nurse had bustled off to get the washing equipment that I had forgotten to grab. We had been left alone, curtained in the cubicle together. He was in the bed, and I stood next to him, blankets and towels under one arm, pillows under the other. He was not a chatter, his only visitor was the hospital chaplain and when she visited she did most of the talking. The ICU nurse was gone ages and so we just stared at each other for a long time. Tchako eventually broke the silence as he asked, 'Are you OK?'

I suppose even that did not break the silence, the tracheostomy renders the voice box useless so I had to lip read.

I mouthed back, 'Sure. You?' It was a hard habit to break that one, making people you just lip-read, lip-read you back. He was not OK.

I knew how to fix that. I'd done counselling module now. I started by pulling a sad face but I thought what Tchako was going through warranted more. One of the counselling lessons had tackled appropriate places to touch people during grief. It was one of the more enjoy-able lectures – I got to shout out all the inappropriate places to touch people; it was a long list. I'd learned that arms were pretty safe, so I put the towels and blankets down on the bed and held his hand, being careful not to inappropriately touch his eyeballs.

My hand on his, I began, 'I am sorry this is happening

to you.' That was me handing out some intensive empathy, now to fire up the rest of this beast of a caring machine. Hold steady now, I told myself. Do not be afraid of asking the big questions and keep them open. The first question was an open question. The training had told me to ask a 'stepping-stone' question to find out his thoughts. 'How are you feeling?' I asked.

Well that was a mistake right there. The counselling lectures had never once considered you would have to lip-read someone's feelings when you are not used to lip-reading. A mood ring and a magic eight ball would have been more use than I was. There was a communication board by the bed, but like all of ICU, it was very perfunctory. Unless he needed to point at a fork or a toilet seat to get his thoughts out, it was useless. I realised that I was best to go for yes/no answers. Not so much a stepping-stone question this time. I went with, 'Are you still thinking about dying?' He did not get time to answer that question.

The curtain snapped back. You forget curtains are not soundproof. Cynthia heard no preamble; she just saw a girl standing in front of a boy, asking him if he still wanted to die, holding a pillow under one arm.

It is incredibly hard to be trusted again after something like that happens. There are no sleeps for anyone on night shifts with this potential psycho of a student around. Tchako was discharged not long after. I had to make up the rest of the case-study essay as I never got put at that bed again. It was an absolute knee-jerk reaction on the part of my facilitators. Even if I had been a threat, I did not understand tracheostomy care. My instinct would have been to put the pillow over his head, which would have done nothing, as all the breathing was going through his neck. It would have taken years to suffocate him; he would have died of constipation with pressure sores to the nose before the pillow did anything.

The essay I did eventually submit was a fairy tale. I obviously left out the bit where I looked to be offering assisted suicide. Instead I wrote a fairy tale in which I unlocked his age-old pain with my wisdom and empathy. Tchako's version of events was no less fanciful than mine when he was finally upright and audible.

Once Tchako found his voice it was hard to shut him up. He sells the story of his miraculous recovery to magazines and the morning shows. There were many photographs of him on the ventilator. (Who took those pictures? We certainly did not, must be the chaplain.) Despite the pictures clearly displaying a ventilator, dialysis and an aortic balloon pump, he attributes his recovery entirely to crystals and herbal medicine. But I can tell you he had one of every big pharma drug in the cupboard. There was no echinacea and milk thistle STAT order. For crying aloud, even the oxygen we pumped around his system was medicalised. Whatever it was that got you through, Tchako, it is just good to see you upright and smiling.

I am taking partial credit for his recovery, though, I did more than the bloody crystals that is for sure. I believe the idiocy of a 20-year-old student nurse and the kerfuffle that followed made Tchako think, *I don't know who these clowns are but I sure as hell need to get away from them quick*. And then the miracle happened?

# ELEVEN

# MEDICAL RECORDS

## 'STAYING ALIVE' BY THE BEE GEES, 'DR. BEAT' BY GLORIA ESTEFAN . . . YOUR TURN.

Your medical notes are called 'Clinical' records for a reason. They were designed to be a stark, comprehensive, contemporaneous, pragmatic and devoid-of-emotion account of a person's medical journey. That is the idea. They are, in fact, contradictory, vast, part fiction and illegible, and most of the time they are missing parts. They are not always a happy read but they are always a page turner. They are, in short, a love letter that lists all of your faults in an attempt to make you better.

The notes are not crisp and pristine. Notes have bits of actual you in them, too, in the form of stains. The notes and you are not allowed to touch each other so it could not possibly be you, could it? I have come across blemishes in notes and said to myself, 'Is that a coffee or chocolate stain?' In the early stages of my career I would sniff it or scratch it off with my nail to find out. It took me a few times to learn, but now when I see these stains my brain is hard wired to yell at me, 'IT IS NEITHER COFFEE NOR CHOCOLATE. NEVER HAS BEEN. NEVER WILL BE. PROTECT YOURSELF. PROTECT THE COLLEAGUES.' I have learned to cover the stain with sticky tape and move on.

You do not get to read your medical story, and if you did you would need an interpreter to make sense of it. It is a collaborative piece comprising both fiction and nonfiction scribbled in diced Latin and Greek sprinkled with acronym. For the uninitiated, I have put together a small glossary of acronyms and a diagram showing where some of your inside bits are. Even if you do not work in health or get diseases, it might help you in a pub quiz.

## SOME OF THE WORDS AND ACRONYMS

In regards to acronyms, there are the tragic, serious ones: CPR (Cardiopulmonary Resuscitation), DNR (do not resuscitate), DOA (dead on arrival). Then there are the acronyms that nurses and doctors don't use anymore, but were funny back in the day: CAH (crazy as hell), PFO (pissed, fell over), FOS (few observable symptoms), FLK (funny-looking kid), FLKLLP (funny-looking kid looked like parents), FUBAR (fucked-up beyond all recognition), GOK (God only knows), LOLINAD (little old lady in no apparent distress), PITA (pain in the arse), PIP (pyjama-induced paralysis).

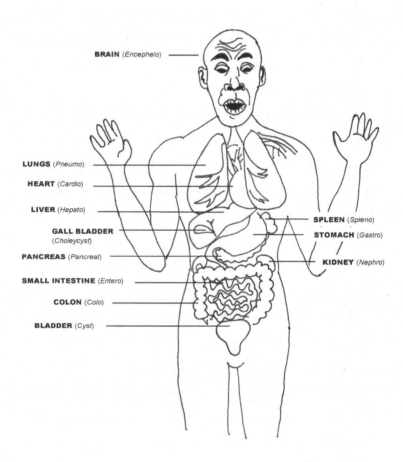

Some medical words are near impossible to pronounce. You may have Pneumonoultramicroscopicsilicovolcanoconiosis. If you say it loud enough, it almost sounds precocious. Lethal black lung to its mates. It is a disease you catch from coal mining or snorting lava. It makes your lungs bleed. I know right, sounds like a nightmare a nine-year-old child would describe to you. Differential diagnosis starts with the physicians asking if the patient can say Pneumonoultramicroscopicsilicovolcanoconiosis without taking a breath; if they can, they do not have it. It is the longest medical word.

Hippopomonstrosesquipedalophobia is the longest word in psychiatry. It means fear of long words. There is me thinking psychiatrists would be kind. Medical science does not make terminology easy. There are many instances where words sound the same but mean different things. Peritoneum and perineum for instance. The peritoneum is the bit of Mel Gibson they slice open before he shouts FREEDOM! in *Braveheart*. Whereas the perineum is the neutral zone in your undercarriage. Often used as a chin rest in intimate social settings but should not be used as such in hospital under any circumstances.

Cervical (referring to the neck vertebrae) and cervical (the bit at the end of a vagina that is supposed to suck sperm up). It is the imperative that you do not mix up these two things. The easy way to remember which is which is to massage Deep Heat into both and see what happens. You will know soon enough and never ever confuse the two again.

In a cruel twist, it would seem the more fun the medical word is to say, often, the more dire the patient's situation. Malignancy, pustulating and the Wenckebach phenomenon are all so much fun to say, but it is not much fun to have them said to you. I've always loved the medical word 'onc'. 'Onc' as in oncology. 'Onc' means cancerous clumps. 'Onc' is such a cute word for such a bitch of a disease. I have always thought the 'onc' bit gives cancer no gravitas, as if you are blowing it a raspberry at it. Oncology sounds like something Beaker from the Muppets might major in.

Sometimes there are just no words to describe medical anomalies. For this we take photographs. Photographs even the dark web would struggle to publish. If a picture can say a thousand words, some of these photos would just be saying 'WTAF?' 250 times.

As you can appreciate with all the oncs and atrophies, notes can often make for a grim read. As with any epic writing, you cannot have tragedy without comedy. Notes are no exception. Here are some of the more ridiculous things we document about you humans.

## THE BRISTOL STOOL CHART (GOOGLE IT IF YOU DARE)

Shitting is vital and universal. So much so that if we cannot make you crap with laxatives and enemas, we will surgically move your bum hole to somewhere else that you still can for a while. For problems of the bowel, we document its activities on the Bristol stool chart.

The Bristol stool chart describes and depicts seven differing stool categories that a human can pass. The 'Bristol' refers to the hospital that created the chart rather than the person. Funny that. Doctors are typically happy to attach their names to even the most horrendous of diseases, such as Parkinson's or Huntington's. But when it comes to a table of turds, they name it geographically.

It was created in 1997. I googled it and shitting had been around and undocumented for quite a while by then. The creators chose to sketch the droppings. It has always struck me as a strange medium to use given that cameras were around.

Seven? There are seven official types? Are we sure, Bristol? I took my family to Bali, and we all got Bali belly, which is a temporary shitting disorder invented by the Devil himself. I reckon we did at least 20 dumps that were not on the chart. We got Bali belly from ice cubes. I reckon we would become less sick and have more fun if next year we holidayed in our backyard and the family all took actual ice.

So far, I have myself achieved six of the seven Bristols, missing only type one, which is described as small, hard like rocks, and difficult to pass. I am not looking forward to that one, but it would be nice to complete the collection. Fours are ideal. They are the sweet spot. They exit the body on command, leaving you with a nice empty feeling. 'Bristol' describes fours as smooth like a sausage, no cracks. This is what you are aiming for kids, I wish you all many fours.

## BOOK-WORK BLOOPERS

I put a call out on my socials for the most joyous things nurses have found in notes. The comments did not disappoint.

✚ **'Pussy wound, requires review.'** It also requires spell check. If a wound is infected with pus, it is pusy not pussy. I am not being pedantic; someone might read that and swab the wrong bit.

✚ **'Past medical history of CABBAGE.'** If a patient had a Coronary Artery Bypass Graft, we document CABG not CABBAGE. While vegetables are the key to a healthy heart, by the time a clot hits, it is a bit late.

✚ **'Patient reluctant to die.'** Perhaps the staff member that penned this was trying to say 'Day 4 of providing end-of-life cares'. It is probably what they meant but it reads more like 'Just get on with it will you, we need the bed'.

✚ **'Patient easily aroused.'** We rouse a patient; we do not arouse them, not on purpose anyway.

That is a different job altogether, one with a lower infection-risk rate and better pay.

✚ **'Patient told me to go fuck myself, will continue to monitor.'** While not entirely professional, this one does get a lot across in just a few words.

✚ **'Patient ate cake, jelly and custard only to vomit a trifle later.'** Bravo to whoever penned this doozy. I hope you gave yourself the rest of the day off for that one.

✚ **'Patient died of death @23:10, nil complications.'** It is short, it is pragmatic, it is almost hopeful. I suppose if you have to die, death would be the best way to do it, especially without complications.

✚ **'Patient hitting it doggy style when he heard a *POP* (penile fracture).'** This was a young doctor's note. You cannot help but think it was their first-time hearing that someone could break a dick. It was the highlight of their internship for sure.

✚ **'Child swallowed several toy pony accessories, comb/bow/stirrup. Condition stable.'** Boom, boom. Slow clap.

✚ **'I love you.'** Many staff, myself included, admitted to accidentally ending a note or a work phone call with 'Love from' or 'I love you' when tired and emotional. What better way to end a love letter? It is embarrassing when it happens but who doesn't need to hear that more.

# TWELVE

# THE NURSES' STATION

### IT PUTS THE LOTION IN THE BASKET, THEN RUBS THE LOTION ON ITS SKIN.

The public debate surrounding a nurse's autonomy largely centres on our relationship with physicians, and the idea that we blindly do what they tell us to do. Can I make it clear that no doctor has ever stood there with a tendon hammer and tried to make that argument? One did once but was promptly told where to shove said hammer. It is more public perception and media portrayal that casts us as doctors' servants.

The nurse/doctor relationship is more symbiotic than that. Yes, nurses do willingly carry out a list of doctors' orders should we find them necessary and correct but we often have a way longer list of jobs to give them back. This is not to say we are equal; the academic achievements of even your basic-model doctor are higher than that of most nurses, but academia is just one measure of intelligence in a field that requires so much of a person. Interns can often be found quivering under a desk on a bad day only to be coaxed out with the promise that they may latch onto the orca nipple and suckle on the tit of knowledge. It is this nourishment that makes some of them grow so big and beautiful.

I suggest that nurse autonomy is instead crippled by policies, procedures, management, mandatory trainings, government legislation and a colleague who loves to highlight things on charts and thinks that everybody else should too.

I belong to a governing body; I am held to account by a nursing code of conduct. I have just read the code of conduct for the first time in possibly two decades. I have stuck to most of the rules by accident, which is a sign of an excellent code. It is certainly very wordy; 4,500 words that pretty much boil down to: 'Treat people how you would want to be treated, try not to sleep with each other and don't gossip about work in the pub.' May I point out all 10 of the Bible's commandments come in at under 70 words. The 10 commandments are a version of a set rules for ALL OF LIFE! I just re-read those for the first time as an adult and they are a lot harder to adhere to, especially as a nurse. It is hard to respecteth the Sabbath when you get 75 per cent shift loading on Sundays. I choose to respecteth the Monday early shift instead.

There are copious annual mandatory updates that hobble nurses. I timed myself doing the last batch: 21 hours all up, most of those hours spent finding the right link and resetting passwords. I know this torture is not unique to nursing and a lot of you are submitted to the same pain. How some industrious, financially strapped registered nurse has not set up an online business where I give them my log-ins and they complete my mandatories for me, I do not know.

Let us talk paperswork. I stick an s in the middle because making the paper singular implies that there is one paper; it is always many papers. If mandatory training hobbles, paperswork is a sledgehammer to the clitoris and balls of a nurse's freedom to nurse. We already did a whole chapter on documentation, but paperswork is something else entirely. Documentation is the necessary bits of a medical story. I consider paperswork to be the less relevant bits. The tick boxes, charts, colour codes, trigger points and assessment tools. Obviously, I am all about making things better, safer, faster and stronger for patients; I just question how giving a group of graduated professionals a box to tick at the start of a shift to confirm that we have indeed introduced ourselves does that.

The never-ending documents and algorithms provide a bullet-proof shield for the organisation should they be filled out pedantically. We can all agree that is a good thing but the endlessness of them leaves the person who missed ticking a box legally vulnerable despite being a gem of a professional. When this happens, the document does not make the system or the patient less safe; instead it is rolled into a scroll with which to bash the employee when things go wrong.

I sound bitter. I suppose on the point of paperswork I am. This is my opinion, but it is also the zeitgeist. There needs to be a limit on what is acceptable in terms of written workload and being micro-managed. Happiness, motivation and job satisfaction are all linked to autonomy.

The paperswork themselves are often lacking in common sense and compassion and fail to recognise patients or staff as people. The documents will be perfect should time cease being a nonspatial continuum and humans become robots. People do not fit in tick boxes.

For instance, the Glasgow coma scale (GCS) is a numbered grading system for a patient's conscious level. A patient scores somewhere between 3 and 15 based on their verbal and motor responses. Fifteen is you right now. If you scull a bottle of wine, you may drop to a 12. Then after a few more bottles, and a couple of Valium, you'll drop down to an eight. An eight is around where we consider getting an anaesthetist to sedate you and pop you on life support. I used to work with a tired old anaesthetist who only opened his eyes to voice, made incomprehensible sounds and could not follow instructions. He was an anaesthetic consultant with a GCS of 7!

Who do you page when the anaesthetist needs intubating?

I also had a ward clerk I adored who would regularly warrant shackling to the bed for her own safety and the safety of others according to the current delirium monitoring paperswork. She was gloriously disruptive and difficult to redirect; she called it running a tight ship. What this means is you regularly fill out a paperswork only to redocument in the notes to explain that regrettably the patient did not fit the chart.

The removal of staffroom toasters seems to be of disproportionate concern to policy shapers, given the life and death situations they could be risk assessing. From time to time a toaster in a staffroom will trigger a fire alarm, sometimes it is my fault, because it is considered poor form to step away from a cardiac arrest to check on the goldenness of my crumpets. The toaster incident very rarely results in anything a firefighter could get excited about, like an actual fire, so they fine the hospitals. Punishing staff by taking away the ability to toast seems overzealous. I have a friend who is in the Country Fire Service and he says that they are always burning toast in the staffroom and they get to keep their toaster. Bloomin' hosepipe hypocrites, the lot of them.

I will not write policy; I will more likely abide by it or make a blooper that generates an incident form requiring the formation of another policy. I will never climb high enough to eradicate bureaucracy. It is unavoidable in a system as big as healthcare. I cannot kill it, but I can take some of the sting out of its tail and here is how: by respecting autonomy, that is, mine and that of others. Like earlobes, fingerprints and twats, each nurse is unique and each one has something different to bring to the party if they are allowed. Those in the system that like to create more paperswork need to remember the party is happening without them. It will still happen if they, the party organiser, has a clipboard telling people where they must sit and when, but no one enjoys that party anymore and they spend a chunk of it bitching about the clipboard lady.

I bring you back to the colleague who loves a high-lighter. For those who love a highlighter, it can become an enjoyable chunk of their day, and for some it becomes an obsession. I helped in day surgery once. Horses for courses but it is not my kind of place. There might have been a lot going on that I was not aware of but from what I could see, it was mostly taking the valuables patients brought in down to the security office and then getting the valuables back again when they woke up. I found myself wanting to ask the bejewelled admissions, 'Did you read the thing in the paperswork we sent you that says please do not bring in any valuables? Would you like us to lock that up with security while you are under anaesthetic or would you like to shelve it during the procedure. You will be asleep, so you will not feel it.

There would be a lot less paperswork that way and so much quicker to retrieve when it's home time.'

Apart from being jewel mule for the shift, I was given one other job. I was trusted with a printed document of the following day's patients and given an orange high-lighter. There were two outcomes; go home (SD) or stay overnight (IP). I was asked to highlight all the ones with SD next to them so it would be easier for the following day's staff to tell at a glance who was same day. It was a 20-page document with two patients on each page. I would have thought the letters SD would have been evidence enough. I handed it back and received feedback that they 'usually use a ruler for underlining upside down so the ink doesn't drag when you pull the ruler off'.

It was then given back to me with a yellow highlighter and I was asked to do all the IPs in yellow. I put it to them that not highlighting all the remaining things was as good as highlighting them a different colour and less effort, and I was told this was how it had always been done. I did not do it, instead I told them I was going outside for a cigarette (I do not smoke; they did not know that) and reflected on the critical feedback I had received. It ended up as a Facebook post about turning a ruler upside down so the ink does not drag. That is bloody genius that is, let us make it a policy.

# THIRTEEN

# PAEDIATRICS UNIT

## KIDS THESE DAYS, AM I RIGHT?

I have chosen never to position myself in paediatrics. The kids are either not medically challenging enough or too ill to bear, the parents are too precious and the maths is too hard. If you get the decimal point in the wrong place on a basic kid's medication, you ruin them. With adults, it is not such an exact science. They only tend to notice the most benign medication errors if they are given via the wrong orifice.

The odd time I have relieved in the Children's Unit I have gone home either disturbed – pinning tiny humans down hard so they do not wriggle while someone sticks medically necessary pins and poisons in them is not for the faint-hearted; or diseased – the pathogen arsenal a snotty or vomity kid carries seems to just flatten them for a couple of days but floors me for a fortnight.

Most of my paediatrics experience has been gained outside of the hospital. I am a nurse with sporty children and so I, and those like me, spend the weekends I am not working providing first aid at my children's sporting and social events. Bring me a bleeding kid and I'll fix them. Controlling blood haemorrhage is a universal life skill. Pressing on the leaky bit and holding it above the heart is something you master in the playground rather than at university; it is intuitive. Bring me a rashy child, I will shit myself. It is probably eczema, but what if it is meningitis or ebola? Abdominal pain can be anything from 'really needs a poo' through to burst appendix. I have a background in Intensive Care so if you need to bring a kid off a pitch in multi-organ failure within an hour of a stroke, then and only then will I have a solid treatment plan.

'Do you think it is broken?' This is a common kids' sport first aider question. There are no positive outcomes for the first aider expected to diagnose limb injuries, especially if the first aider does not have X-ray vision. The exchange can go one of two ways.

*A*

**Concerned parent:** Do you think it is broken?

**First aider:** It'll be right that, just needs to jog it off.

*Kid re-enters game, in the first tackle the misdiagnosed, already broken bone now compounds, forcing its way out of the skin, gouging another kid's eye out and leaving the well-meaning first aider thoroughly disliked by all and legally culpable.*

**B**

**Concerned Parent:** Do you think it's broken?

**First aider:** I'm not sure. I never think it's broken. You could go get an X-ray just in case.

*Team loses match as star player and his Munchausen mother go to Emergency department. You receive a text the following day. 'What a waste of time that was. Sat there for five hours and they did nothing, just Panadol, nothing! This patient went bunta and smashed an automatic door with a wheelchair and then he just pulled his pants down and defecated right there in the smashed glass, all in front of the children. And anyway the toe wasn't broken after all; it was just a fracture.'*

A couple of things, Cathy. Firstly, triage assessed your boy as having a non-life-threatening injury and gave him Panadol, a clerk put him on the system, a doctor and radiographer combined to order, complete and report the fracture on an X-ray. The doctor and radiographer had been to school long enough to learn that fracture and break mean exactly the same thing, your son's fractured toe is also by default broken. A security team stopped you and your boy getting assaulted or shat on and a cleaner got rid of a turd with sharp glass embedded in it. So you are right, Cathy. No one did anything. Secondly, can we stop for a second and appreciate the skill, power and brilliance of the glass-shard shitter, the star of this text. The very purpose of an automatic door is that it opens when things approach, he threw the wheelchair quicker than the sensors could sense. He beat the space–time continuum.

Nurse's children rarely get X-rays in the first day or so post injury. There is always some home-brand differential diagnosing system first. If I am clearing one of mine for a fracture, for instance in the arm, I wait till they are hypnotised by the TV and shout 'keeper' then lob a tin of baked beans at them. If they catch it with both hands, no X-ray. If they catch with the non-affected limb only, proceed to X-ray. If it is a bad shot and they do NOT catch it, they score a head MRI too.

I am not without heart. Tom, my eldest, had his forearm in a cast for six weeks after he broke it on his 14th birthday in a match. He was angry the whole time the cast was on. Poor fella had only just discovered masturbation and he got benched. He was a terribly angry boy till that cast came off.

All nurses are mandated reporters. We are mandated to report suspected mistreatment or misuse of all children be they in hospital or in the wild. We might not be the bench-mark for perfect parenting but we are ideally placed to spot a child who is living a cruel existence and we have the right constitution to be bothered in a useful way.

There is a mandatory reporting training module biannually. This is so we can spot the subtle differences between our own tough parenting that builds character and soul-destroying abuse that needs dobbing in. Once I realised the reporting was not about saying 'how evil are those parents' and all about asking 'how safe are the children?', reporting became less harrowing and more doable. The mandatory reporting modules are always delivered by a lady who more than likely throws contact-free karate birthdays parties for her own exceedingly safe but perilously anxious kids.

In the competency training session, the mandatory reporting trainer will say: 'OK, we're going to talk about some scenarios, and you are all going to tell me about how worried you are about the children involved. You have a neighbour who has children of lower primary school age who are often seen fighting, unattended on the trampoline, inappropriately dressed for the weather. The mother is only ever seen when she comes outside to shout at the children and the bin is always full of empty alcohol bottles. How worried are we?'

Me: 'I am very worried, but not about the children. I'm very worried you are talking about my house.'

You do get left with the feeling that the whole session could be better put across with a slogan: 'If you come across a scenario that makes you think, *This looks like the start of a very dark Netflix documentary*, report it.'

My perspective on what constitutes a healthy environment for children has changed dramatically since raising my own. As a student I wrote a reflective piece about a 43-year-old mother we had visited who had twin babies. The sink was overflowing with plates and the fruit in the fruit bowl was mouldy. The floor was scattered with nappy bags; the mother was still in pyjamas in the afternoon. A bit judgy, for sure. If I had had twins at my age I would never not be in pyjamas, and I would only eat ready meals off paper plates.

Tom, my eldest, has a mandatory report with his name on it following a head injury when he was eight or nine. He fell off a bicycle while not wearing a helmet in a park. It was a wonderfully slapstick moment. He was going down a paved incline hurtling forward but looking backwards shouting, 'Look at this, Mum.' I looked up just in time to see his bike hit a small wall and Tom fly over it.

Heads bleed a lot and he warranted a hospital visit because there was also face damage. Now, rightly or wrongly (mostly wrongly), on the way to the hospital, I asked Tom to lie. It is the law in our state that all cyclists wear helmets and I did not want to get in trouble.

So, although I am married and live with Steve, the biological daddy of both the children, I told Tom to say, 'It was ma dad's weekend to have me and he doesn't think about things like that.'

Steve absolutely does think of things like that. He is an accountant; accountants are not thrill seekers. If Steve took the children out on the bikes, he would put them in helmets and knee pads and elbow pads and a condom in case they fell off the bike onto an arse. I promised Tom something from the hospital vending machine if he helped me out. I had forgotten that of course head injuries and plastic surgery cases are fasted until review. The wait in triage and the lack of promised chocolate put Tom in such a bad mood with me that by the time the doctor gave the helmet safety pamphlet and lecture Tom looked at me and said to the doctor, 'I really want a cycle helmet, but Mum says I can't have one because cycle helmets are for pussies.'

Tom sustained no long-term physical scarring, but I reckon there might be some psychological damage given the fact the only clean thing I had in the park for a head bleed was a sanitary napkin. One day he will remember how he proudly showed this special dressing that stuck to his hand to all the doctors and nurses as he read them the trivia on the sticky back protector wrap.

My other son Robbie also has a singular mandatory report on him because you cannot play favourites.

Robbie was awarded his in his very first few weeks of primary school. In the first week of school, Robbie was sent home with impetigo (a skin infection). Impetigo starts off looking like a cigarette burn then it grows. Robbie's impetigo was on his neck and forearms, it made him look very unloved and perhaps this had the school on high alert.

Robbie was returned to school post infection and during the first day back, there was a session with the pastoral support worker and all the new school settlers. Presumably, it was a dull session because Rob chose to attempt to provide some light relief. The support worker asked how each of the little ones felt about school. Little Lucy said she loved it because she got to walk in with Grandma. Asher said he loved that he could play army at lunch with new friends.

When she asked Robbie, he simply said, 'I don't like it because Michael Jackson sticks his fingers in my arsehole.'

Robbie had expected laughter to follow his statement and it did not happen and instead he was just stared at. Mortified, he curled up in a ball and would not get up until the audience had been evacuated and the teacher had uncurled him with kindness. As a standup, I can very much feel Robbie's pain here.

Let us unpack what happened. There are several things that went wrong. Can you spot them? Let us start with the tense: 'sticks'. 'Michael Jackson sticks.'

He could not indeed 'stick' as he had been dead for two years at this point. He could have 'stuck' had they ever met or indeed been in the same country at any point, but they were not.

The other thing that went wrong here is that Robbie said this to a member of school staff, who are also mandatory reporters. I am grateful to the reporter for keeping an eye out for my son but read the room, kid! The pastoral support worker was less worried about grammar and likelihood of Robbie and MJ hanging out together and instead worried about a young boy who had made an allegation of a sexual nature and then become distressed. *Where would a five-year-old even learn such a thing to say?* she thought to herself. A five-year-old learns such things if he is listening in on his nurse mother and her mates spending an afternoon on bitch diesel wetting themselves at such sentences. I clearly remember saying that exact sentence a good two years before and my husband exploding with laughter. It must have been that that made it stick for Robbie.

The parenting role is one where the main aim is to work your way to redundancy. On the whole, nurses are great at this although we all have that colleague who cannot quite let the job go. I used to work with a woman who would relish the time her fully adult son spent out of the home as it would give her the chance to 'get stuck into his bedroom'. Get him on a sticker chart, Narelle;

he's 42, love. You cannot help thinking it is a little bit more about Narelle than the son there.

Now that I have teenagers, I feel the impending redundancy acutely. Nurses raise tough little bastards. We see everything in the hospital. We understand that life can be anything from a comfortable struggle right through to uninhabitable. Not all things can be aided by resilience and good attitude, but they are helpful in most instances. We prepare the kid for the path not the path for the kid. I devoted absolutely no parenting time when both of mine cried over someone they had never nor would ever meet burning their imaginary ladder on Minecraft. They are going to need way more resilience and coping strategies than that to cope with buttoning up a shirt with Parkinson's, for instance.

For the child of a nurse, the dinner table is where the nurse adult chooses to deliver traumatic life lessons. Stories from the frontlines of sex, drugs, suicide, violence, STIs, alcohol. All the cheery stuff. If the topic is extremely difficult, they will deliver their sermons in the car so the child cannot escape the life preparations. Sometimes when the nurse parent talks, they are not entirely sure if they are kitting the child out for complex realities to come or just giving the child terribly fun ideas of things to do at the weekend. You can see a glint in the nurse parent's eye as they deliver teachings that belie the fact they have done the bad stuff, enjoyed it and survived. Many of the moments when they have felt truly alive they were doing something their own parents would disapprove of.

Let us hear it for the Paediatric nurses, people. At the heart of what a nurse is, it is someone who treats the patient in front of them as if they were their family. Paediatric nurses, for obvious reasons cannot do this, they would be sued. They have to treat the hospital children better than they would their own children and for this we applaud them.

# FOURTEEN

# ALLIED HEALTH DEPARTMENT

## THE UNSUNG HEROES OF THE HOSPITAL.

Let us shine a pen torch on the Allied Health department just this once then forget about them instantly. In no particular order.

## SPEECH PATHOLOGY

Speech pathologists have just two things to remedy: *dysphasia* and *dysphagia*. One means compromised swallowing and the other means compromised speaking. Nobody, not even speech pathologists, knows which is which. Ironic that the people in charge of spoken word could not think of two that sounded different in any way.

They are the Mary Poppins of the hospital as far as no one really knows how to summon one, but they always appear when somebody needs them most, even if that someone does not know how to ask. They are practically perfect in every way and they help the medicine go down.

If there were a suggestive hospital staff calendar in Allied Health, I would think speech path would take the spring months clad in just a well-ironed frilled pinafore and heels so high it would suggest they do not walk around the hospital, rather they float.

They are more patient than nurses. I saw a film where a speech pathologist helped a man learn to communicate using his sole remaining independently moving part: a solitary eyelid. She then supported him in writing *The Diving Bell and the Butterfly*. It became a very successful book and feature film about his experiences. That is some stubborn dedication. Very touching, but I reckon a nurse would get two sentences in and be like, 'Do you know what I think would work better than a book about your journey? A short poem. Or a tweet.'

This profession appears gentle, however, speech paths essentially throw biscuits at the ailing to see which ones will choke and which ones won't. That is badass. They absolutely will not let them starve though, instead they prescribe 'thickened fluids', which is water the texture of yogurt, and 'minced diet', which means look forward to a main meal of a more pourable consistency.

## DIETICIANS

The dieticians will take whatever paltry regimen the speech pathologists have instigated and then proceed to remove any of the remaining fun, salt and sugar. They will then be alarmed that you have a poor appetite. This is known as victim blaming.

Dieticians assess the healthiness of a person's weight using a BMI chart. The chart is fundamentally flawed, men get to weigh more than women, which makes no sense. I have breasts and hips. Unless a man has testicles that jiggle out of a G cup when they break into a brisk walk, then I should get to be heavier surely.

The dieticians are a contrary bunch. They spend most of your life telling you to stop eating things but redeem themselves in your frailer autumn years by bargaining with you to get you to eat anything you like. Jelly seems good to go at any point in your timeline; dieticians must have shares in a jelly company or something.

In the calendar, they will represent the summer months. People imagine dieticians to have bikini-beach bodies but instead they seem have more glorious 'lived-in' versions, ones with a bit more about them. Bodies that suggest they know how to behave but still sometimes do not. Mmmmm, saucy! (Try using a low-fat protein-based yogurt in the sauce rather than full cream though.)

In the calendar, I suggest they are naked; they will be fine with that. They will be dancing and shaking their perfectly wobbly bits behind ginormous neon jelly structures. They love jelly, like figuratively you cannot handle all the jelly that they have.

## PHYSIOTHERAPISTS (PT)

Physiotherapists handle the correcting of muscle injuries. Muscle damage presents in one of two ways.

> Acute, meaning it will get better by itself without a physio.
> Or . . .
> Chronic, meaning it will never get better no matter what the physio does.

For either type, the physio will dish you out an exercise to do very slowly 10 times each day. This will help not a jot, mainly because despite having all day to do the exercise you will never get around to it.

I, like many nurses, have chronic Plantar fasciitis. It is a heel pain prevalent in people who spend a lot of time on their feet or the obese. I doubled down there. Also known as flip-flop foot, you can catch it from living a thong-based existence. How bloody Australian is that. A physio told me to fix this by drawing a tea towel towards myself with my toes for two minutes each morning, 'with your morning cuppa so you do not forget, Mrs Carroll'. The pain is insane so I tried this exercise once. It was so boring that I decided I would rather have pain and limp than start my day in such a tedious fashion.

Did you hear the story about the physiotherapy Christmas party? No? That is because no one ever talks about physio parties. They are quite the sensible, serious crowd.

They are also expressionless lovers; I know this because we have simulated sex many times in various leg, back and hip assessments and they give me nothing in the face, even when I wink at them and bite my lower lip.

Physios are, however, anatomically perfect so they should fit anywhere in the calendar. They are Vitruvian; they simply do not make ugly physios. If you apply to be a physio and you look less than plainly perfect, you get redirected to the podiatry or social-work school. The problem is physios do not know how to make the best of themselves.

In the calendar, they would be January, a pointless month where you exercise a limp form of self-discipline with no actual results. They would be wearing track pants and a polo shirt as they seem incapable of wearing anything form-fitting.

## OCCUPATIONAL HEALTH (OT)

Occupational therapists are the lesser-known cousins of the physios. They are a nervous herd who see potential danger everywhere. Even rugs are fraught with danger according to OTs. What they lack in courage, they more than make up for with generous hearts and good intentions.

They have the exceedingly difficult job of convincing people who have fought in wars or created empires that they can only be discharged from hospital after they prove they are safe around kettles.

OT appointments sound like this.

> **OT:** 'I have supplied a commode for when you go home because your bathroom is upstairs.'
>
> **Patient:** 'I've pissed in my kitchen sink for years and I'm not stopping now.'
>
> **OT:** 'You might find that a little harder now your hip is broken, madam.'

There is nothing sexier than generosity and a luxurious, Christmassy, Madonna-esque material girl shoot with an elderly infirm woman, in full bling and feather fans, teetering on stilettoes down a staircase waving her walking frame in the air. OTs dance in tuxedos on either side of her with big smiles trying to gift her sensible shoes and toilet-seat raisers while she plays hard to get. That is if the OTs are not too scared of the stairs to do the shoot.

## SOCIAL WORKERS

For each of us, depending on our politics, one of the following statements is true.

Social workers strive to create a more socially just society by supporting people of all ages and abilities to lead more fulfilling lives.

Or . . .

Social workers are form-filling, folder-holding, tie-dye wearing, tax-dollar thieving whingers who steal children, imprison the elderly, fund the lazy and free the nutters.

Both statements have an element of truth to them and herein lies the problem. We all want a socially just society, but it requires redistribution of funds and opportunity and that is the bit about which we are all less united. For those without to get more, those with need to give something away. This is the fly in the cannabis oil.

I have *enough money* and I am generous with it, but I do understand the anxieties of those who believe redistributing their hard-earned cash to the 'can't work, don't work' crew is enabling rather than helping, because I feel the same way about food. Even when I have more than enough, I do not want to share. If you want chips, get a job and buy your own chips. You get that first one for free, but I am going to stab my plastic spork through your thieving little mitt if it so much as thinks about coming in for another one, you freaky seagull witch.

Social workers would have their own handcrafted, recycled lunar calendar. Uranus would be circling a full moon. Saturn's ring would be out in all its glory. Saturn would be up for that; she was a hoot to work with.

## PODIATRY

The punk rockers of allied health. They burn toes and cut bits off feet, smiling while they do it. Then they get out their little handheld vacuum and hoover up the evidence like it's nothing.

They are quirky; I have a podiatrist friend who has a phobia of old potatoes with eyes in them (potatomattophobia) but no fear of decaying fungus feet. I want to be supportive, but I feel she has life the wrong way around.

A lot of their clientele cannot feel their feet. I met a man who did not know he had lost a few toes until a doctor told him. He had not seen or felt them for an awfully long time, so he did not know exactly where or when they went. Imagine that. I know where the toes went because he told his story while I was in his home dressing his toe stumps while a litter of puppies chewed the toes of the other foot. When I shooed the puppies away, the patient barked, 'LEAVE 'EM! They're only playing.'

Numb feet are a phenomenon the doctors call peripheral neuropathy; they believe it to be an unfortunate by-product of poorly controlled diabetes. I believe numb feet to be an absolute godsend for diabetics given the sadistic shit podiatrists inflict.

In the sexy calendar, they would take the winter months. We are not talking snowy scenes with log fires. The backdrop would be a harsh hailstone blizzard. The podiatrist would be naked save for a gimp mask face and clumpy Velcro-fastening orthotic shoes. They would be wielding a flamethrower in one hand and a handy vac in the other.

# FIFTEEN

# SEXUAL
# HEALTH CLINIC

### OOH, ER, MISSUS.

Sex can be quite an uncomfortable conversation depending on your value system and experiences with it. I have had only kind sexual experiences and my value system can be best described as 'I would do anything for love, yes even that'. I have written the following paragraph as a canary down the mine, which sounds like a sex manoeuvre, but it is not. It is intended to be a gauge to see how open you will be to this chapter. Use it to calibrate your sensitivity to my funny, filthy talk. We might need a safety word; let us go with 'MERCY'.

In my birth town, we had a group of low public housing tower blocks called the seven sisters. Bestiality film makers were busted there after police spotted the production crew trying to get a donkey in a lift. I believe the ass was pivotal to the plot. The donkey was being stubborn as a mule about getting in the lift, which was the troupe's downfall but a definite win for the donkey. The troupe leader denied that the animal was for sexual purposes. I bet Eeyore, Eeyore, Eeyore-ways says that.

If you enjoyed reading that as much as I enjoyed writing it, then please proceed to enjoy the next few pages. If you found yourself shouting 'MERCY' then muttering 'well that was unnecessary' then please flick forward to page 189. If it made you tingle, go give yourself a minute. The rest of us can wait.

The sin of lust can be described as an unbridled desire for something to the point that it becomes a downfall. Lust is usually associated with intense longing for forbidden sex acts but it can also be used to describe an all-consuming craving for money and power. This section will focus on the sex bit because if your inner drive is screaming at you to be a soulless millionaire megalomaniac, then nursing is probably not the way to do it. Big pharma might be.

My husband and I have never given our boys 'the talk' as such. Instead we have dished out snippets of the whole story at traffic lights or some plot line on *Glee* or *Riverdale* has prompted a discussion about 'so if someone is drunk, can they consent?'. My mum took me to a sleepy village in Wales to give me 'the talk'. She sold it as a mum and daughter weekend, and I remember really looking forward to it. I was prepubescent and how much do you love one-on-one time with your adults as a small child?

Apparently, there was going to be a special someone, and I was going to fall madly in love with 'him' before I did 'it'. She went through the mechanics of what 'it' was, along with what went where. She was aided by a manual of some sort. I was absolutely on board until she said he would put it in and out and in and out and in and out and that absolute horror story completely ruined our trip. Losing my virginity was not as Mum had foretold; it was neither nightmare nor fairy tale. I waited and waited for the right 'him' but became impatient by 18 and asked a friend, J, if he would not mind 'doing it with me' to get it out of the way. We were not madly in love and neither he nor I minded. I had worried needlessly about the whole in and out again and again, it was actually a highlight of the whole event.

You do not need to do the birds and bees talk now. All the basics are taught at school, and I would argue that in the primary-school years my boys had more hours of personal development and reproduction teaching than I had hours of actual sex. You want your children to know they can come to you or a trusted adult or else they will ask the internet, and nobody wants that. Google anything to do with sex and you are only ever three clicks away from a man in a cowboy hat rubbing his balls on stinging nettles for gratification. Did somebody just say 'MERCY'? Toughen up. This is still a less traumatic picture to me than Mum telling me it goes in and out repeatedly.

In order to arm the kids with what they need so that lust does not ruin either them or others, I back up school facts with a general vibe that anything is acceptable so long as it is safe and leaves all the people involved feeling good about themselves. I could tell them exactly what to do and when the right time is and who the right person is but you cannot tell a teenager anything without them disagreeing. To prove a point, my 16-year-old constantly corrects David Attenborough during nature documentaries. You cannot correct Sir David Attenborough about animals; he invented animals.

I tend to just correct or enjoy the kids' misconceptions now. Tom once claimed that in America there were 17 people in a Jacuzzi and only one of them was a man, and he came and all 16 women got pregnant. Look, if he thinks it is that easy, who am I to correct him? After a putting-a-condom-on-a-cucumber education session in year 8, Rob came home with one question, 'I get why we put the condom on, but what is the cucumber for?'. I was very tempted to say you pop one in every hole and then leave the room, that is very safe sex.

When you see the things you see in healthcare, it is hard to hit the right note when preparing children for the adult world. In a medical sense, sex with partners is risky enough but it is more often what people get up to on their own that causes them to come to the Emergency department. Please understand that if you yourself have had to have medical help to remove something that got stuck in a bottom/vagina/urethra then there is no judgement here. I enjoy an orgasm as much as the next person, and if that was the only way I could get there, I would try it. Luckily it is very much not.

So far as sexual pleasure goes, so long as everyone involved is able to consent and wants to be there, any injuries sustained are no worse than a tennis elbow. I have dedicated no chapters to tennis elbow because no one is interested in injuries caused by a sweaty racquet grip unless the sweaty racquet grip went somewhere its manufacturers did not design it to go. We all have kinks; if this is yours then here are a few ways that you can do it safely.

If the option is open to you, be sure to use parts of another human. Willing people are not always readily available but they are perfect for the purpose and rarely, if ever, does anyone get a whole person lost inside of them. If you have no consenting humans then of course use what you can, but planning is important. Use something with a wide base, nail it to a wall or attach it to some sturdy rope. If, however, something does go astray, be sure to seek medical opinion. You need a friend at that point and we can be that.

At parties, people always ask nurses about the strangest thing they ever found up someone. I will always answer but with folklore finds rather than first-hand, eye-witness accounts because each person's medical mining journey is so specific that you could be commanding a crowd with joyful anecdotes of snow globes that needed draining and filling with plaster before removal or stories of firemen being called to cut the end of a wine bottle off to release suction and should the poor victim be in the room there is no way they would think, *They are probably taking about someone else who also fell on a snow globe then a bottle.* I feel they have been through enough already and I prize their dignity as much as my registration. I do always have a 'story' on hand because I do love attention.

The sex acts that are deemed forbidden and damaging to social order are changeable and depend on many factors; generation, religion and geography being the more notable ones. Coitus before marriage was forbidden in my grandma's generation. Many of her age have stories of babies they birthed in secret and then had removed for the shame of it. Society has moved on in many ways but the teenage mum and the bastard child are still often socially synonymous with disgrace. In the olden days forced sex by a husband could not legally be considered rape, and this is often still the case in practicality. Sodomy between two males was forbidden, indeed illegal, in Australia until 1994 and is still illegal in over

70 countries. Even in today's Western society there is a constant evolution of what is publicly palatable or legal. This is of no concern to a healthcare system. A nurse's job is to respect people's sexuality, educate them on how to be safe about it, remedy any complications that arise from it and advocate and protect when choice was not involved. We leave the donkey's sexual health to the police and vets.

*No animals were harmed in this story. At least not after the donkey, goat, chickens and python were all safely rehomed.

# SIXTEEN

# WOMEN'S HEALTH

NO TWO TWATS ARE THE SAME. I VERY
MUCH QUESTION THE MOTIVES OF THE
RESEARCHERS ON THAT PROJECT.

## FEMALE GENITALIA

I learned the female external sex organ from a medical-teaching model. We were to learn how to insert a urinary indwelling catheter (IDC/medical piss pipe). The model had genitalia the likes of which I would never see again, thankfully. If you can imagine, the model was a woman on her back. The mannequin has been cut off from the flat-tummied belly button upwards and the legs had been severed with just enough left to give the idea of being wilfully akimbo. The most unique thing about this fanny was that a chunk of the party section was missing, clearly a bite injury.

The lecturer, a limp, quiet man, began the practical assessment with a disclaimer. His house had been broken into, and the robbers had found his bag full of medical teaching props and the thieves had damaged the contents. They had taken a clean bite out of the female and the practice penis shaft was no longer available due to irreparable damage during the robbery. The burglar had been caught on the instructor's home-surveillance system. The burglar had worked alone. To this day, I would offer the lecturer a bite-sized chunk out of mine to watch that footage. I am never not thinking about it.

I was successful at inserting the urethral catheter into the defaced prop. Stellar work given the lack of identifiable landmarks. The lab assessment (not to be confused with labia assessment; there were none) was a ridiculous role-play requiring me to get informed consent from a headless vandalised bit of plastic.

My first live catheterisation was more ridiculous still. The patient's belly was not flat; she had an apron of fat that drowned the mons pubis denying me access to the target unless two nurses took shifts holding the belly out of the way. My patient's legs were not so much wilfully akimbo; they were instead violently kicking out. There was something about the way she spat that made me feel the Russian she was yelling was not informed consent.

I used four catheters in all that day: two up the vulva, one to bash away at the clitoris for a while before landing one in the urethral meatus (pee hole), which had hidden itself on the ceiling of the vagina. Finding a lady's pee hole is difficult at the best of times, but when they go hiding like that it can be impossible. The woman was so relieved as her bladder emptied that she kissed me full on the mouth then put the heavy apron to good use with belly laughs. I hope this was to do with the bladder emptying rather than the hammering I gave her G-spot.

I understand the coyness when people are asked to take them knickers off and crack it open for a medical professional. I love nudity. I go to nude beaches but there is something so private about private holes. For instance, I would be happy to show my arse at the staff Christmas party, but I may never go to work again if I showed them my arsehole.

Please understand if you are putting off a pap smear because of shyness, you must not. Health professionals are unphased by holes. We can pull yards of vaginal packing tape out of you and think about slow-cooker recipes at the same time. Once you have stripped down to T-shirt and nothing from the waist down (fortunately for me this is my best look), pop your heels together, fling your knees apart, and find something to focus on on the ceiling. Avoid conversation. There is nothing to be said at a time like this that would make anyone more comfortable.

Examples of failed conversations I have overheard during internals.

**Consultant:** 'OK, if you look here, what can you see?' (Consultant beams head torch at patient's chuff.)

**Intern:** 'I can see, er . . . some signs of aging?'

**Lady on barouche:** 'Yup, top marks, doctor. It is approximately the same age as the rest of me.'

Or . . .

**GP:** 'Have you thought any more about losing weight?'

**Lady, laid pant-less and splayed on bed:** 'I've lost a bit; you are not looking at my best angle. I am still sitting around 110 but as you can see from where you are, none of that is sitting around the heart so I would not concern yourself.'

For privacy, the practice nurse or doctor will shroud your lower half in what they call a dignity cloth. This of course makes you instantly forget what they are looking at.

If you find yourself growing more confident while receiving this procedure over the years, try whipping the cloth off and staring them down. You can start with baby steps, just lifting and lowering the cloth saying, 'Where's she gone? There she is' over and over.

## MENSTRUATION

I get the point of periods, but does anyone else, like me, feel that there are just far too many of them? If you get the proper egg allocation and lifespan as a woman, you will shed around 450 eggs. Some will turn into people if you want; some will even if you did not want them to. You can use some of them but for heaven's sake do not try to use them all.

The most babies anyone ever made is Mrs Vasilyeva recorded at 69 births. All multiple births. For crying out loud, woman. The Guinness Book of Records does not credit her a first name. I reckon it was just Mum by the end. There are too many periods and they start too young. A 10-year-old has no idea what is happening. My very first period my father handed me a sanitary towel and said have the day off school. I used that day to decorate said napkin with bubble writing in glitter pens to say, 'Georgie's room, no boys allowed!!!' and stuck it on my bedroom door whilst free-bleeding onto my thighs and mattress.

Menstruation is a messy business. I am a capable woman, but I have never been successful with periods. I usually bleed on something. It affects my confidence not a jot. I do not lose pre-acquired skills or power of reason as is often implied of a woman on the blob. But neither do I develop the ability to rollerskate and skydive after uploading tampons, which is disappointing though I do admit I have not tried all the brands.

Too many and too messy. I can only imagine how pointless this monthly debacle seems to those who never want to make the periods into people. More so, to those who long for babies and struggle to have them. It seems almost cruel the way a female body signals another month of lost hope with cramps and blood. I always thought perhaps the fanny could fire out a Kinder egg with a little sorry note inside instead on these occasions.

## INTERNAL ORGANS

A female foetus is fitted with all the reproductive gear she may or may not need through the first half of her life. By the time a woman hits her 40s, most of her drinking circle will be discussing the logistics of getting the now malfunctioning clobber surgically removed before the walls cave in and the infrastructure removes itself.

I have had one gynae reboot so far, for stress incontinence. This means you laugh when you piss. Sorry – wrong way round, that is a mental-health issue. It means you piss when you laugh. Stress incontinence is highly inconvenient given my job as a standup. I met a man with narcolepsy (sudden attacks of sleep) and sleep apnoea (stops breathing when asleep) so I fully understand some people are dealt worse hands than I.

Sometimes stress incontinence can be fixed with Kegels. These are the pelvic-floor exercises that no one can see you doing. Exactly what is the point of doing any exercise if you cannot put a picture of you doing it on Instagram? I scored an eight-week ban for my Insta Kegels montage #kegels #nofilter #feelingcutemightdeletelater #suckitup.

I needed a kink surgically put in my urethra. This would have been relatively painless if it had been keyhole. The operation was not keyhole because surgeons use any of the body's predrilled holes as a tradesman's entrance when possible.

To get access to the internal plumbing pipes with scalpels, the external flaps need to be pegged open intra operatively. I do not know how they do this, having never been a theatre nurse. I would have hoped they used a couple of cushioned marshmallow tongs applying the gentle un-pinching motion you use to enlarge a picture on your smart phone. I think what they actually did was put a bulldog clip on each majora, then tied a shire horse to each clip with thick rope then fired a gun so the horses bolted in opposite directions.

If nothing else comes from this book, I hope it triggers some young medical mind to think of a better way.

My grandma's lady innards had been re-stumped that many times with hammocks, rings, planks and slings that if we did a pelvic X-ray, she would have looked like an orangutan play area. It is no wonder she fell over a lot. My mother has embarked on the same medical journey and has informed me that I will follow. Now there is something to look forward to. I worry sometimes that I will laugh too hard on stage one day and take someone's eye out with my cervix. I would leave it swinging. It would be a tripping hazard but worth it for me to not be hooked up to the horses again.

# CLITTERY GLOSSARY

**KEGELS:** (m/f/x) Imagine you are trying to suck ET back up into the UFO, the UFO being your vagina. ET being imaginary. There you go, that's it, that right, there is a Kegel. These are done by both women and men to improve sexual function or symptoms of urinary incontinence. Men, to Kegel, imagine you can teleport ET through your peritoneum using the force. Do not use a real ET, he has been through enough. Feel free to use the force if you possess it, young padawan. These exercises should only be performed at traffic lights, for some reason.

**LABIUM MAJORA:** (f/x) The meaty outer flaps, part-pubed skin and part whatever that other slimy skin is. Often confused with labia minora, which is all about frilly slimy skin.

**PAP SMEAR:** (f/x) You are overdue. Make time; get it done, please. Non-negotiable.

**URETHRAL MEATUS:** (m/f/x) Hole to pee out of or stick a piss pipe in.

**VAGINAL PACKING TAPE:** (f/x) A sterile, gauze,

never-ending scarf inserted into a vagina. I am not sure why, probably anti-haemorrhage related. Put in under general anaesthetic but pulled out over a several minutes of polite conversation while the lady is fully awake! Too much!

**WHATEVER THAT OTHER SLIMY SKIN IS:** (f/x) Words like epithelial, discharge and pH are bandied about, but medicine has yet to come up with a conclusive term.

# SEVENTEEN

# MEN'S HEALTH

## CAUTION, MAY CONTAIN NUTS.

This is a story of my husband and a lump. I will tell you from the beginning that the lump was non-life threatening and is long since removed and is now in a bin, living a full life with all his medical-waste friends. I tell you this at the beginning otherwise you will worry about him (Steve, not the lump). I use this story to demonstrate the male reluctance to seek medical help. It is a tale of a Steve who woke up with one less testicle than the day before and still did not believe he required medical review.

Shortly before my husband Steve's 40th, he received a letter from the GP calling him for a mid-life, well-man check-up. Given that the celebration theme was to be 40 days and 40 nights of things Steve loves:

pubs, cigarettes, sport watching, stressing about other peoples' bad driving, red foods and me, he probably should have done the check-up before rather than after. By after I mean he was nearer to 50 than 40 by the time I had done enough nagging to get him there. He has shocking genetic predispositions on his father's side, so he needs monitoring. He came home very smug. My pestering had been unnecessary, as according to Steve, our GP had said he was in tip-top condition. He just had to eat more salmon for a slight vitamin-D deficiency. He was clutching a large paper pharmacy bag as he told me this.

'That bag got salmon in it has it, Steve?'

I had a rifle through the bag, and it contained atenolol, perindopril and a statin. I love our GP. She is clever and thorough, and she explains things well. There was no way she prescribed these things without talking him through high blood pressure and cholesterol, and how they link to smoking, stress and inactivity. If she weighed him, which she would have, no part of her care plan would have mentioned eating more of anything. I did try to reinforce all these things later as he picked his way around a tofu stir-fry only to be told that I was not a doctor. Anyway, back to the lump and what we did about it.

I had heard him tittering and grumbling from the bedroom while I was showering in the en suite. I cut my shower short as the twittering became shouting with a tone to it that suggested maybe the fabled home invasion had commenced.

'GEORGE! QUICK!'

There was no gunman, just Steve, bed spread flipped aside, PJs and undies around his ankles, in the pap position frisking his nuts.

'SOMETHING'S NOT RIGHT!'

My turn to frisk. *8 am is too early for this shit!* I thought.

Me: 'Well, it's a long time since I've seen them sober, but you know how you used to have two bollocks, right? Well, you just have one big one now.'

Steve: 'WHAT! WHAT DO YOU MEAN? WHAT DOES THAT LOOK LIKE?'

Why on earth you would ask your nurse/comedian wife to describe that car crash of a scrotum I do not know.

Me: 'It's big, shiny . . . bouncy . . . space-hopper bouncy. You could bounce around the cul-de-sac on it if you wanted. It's all in the balls. The dick is still there mostly, what I can see of it anyway. It's been engulfed by the ball. Like cyclops, if the eye was a dick. It looks like Pac-Man eating a vol-au-vent.'

Steve: 'Steady on, wife! Should we put some Savlon on it? Get the Savlon. WHAT *ARE* YOU DOING?'

Me: 'I'm taking a picture for you.'

Steve: 'DON'T! Do not take a picture of it. Jesus, George, that will be in a cloud now. Could be anywhere.

That could just *pop up* in a work meeting on PowerPoint! That could just land on the kid's iPads.'

Me: 'Well, you wanted the kids off Minecraft.'

I should explain why I was taking a picture. Steve could not fully self-assess his own undercarriage as he cannot see it past his belly. I am in no way complaining about the belly. I fed it; I like a bear of a man. I have never fancied anyone who weighed less than me; that would make me feel undainty. Hence the photograph. Steve is happy with me telling any part of this story except for this bit. I do not think of it as private because anyone looking at him, even with his clothes on, would assume this was the case. However, in the interests of preserving his dignity and my marriage, let us pretend that Steve could not self-assess because although he has a toned six pack and an enormous penis, unfortunately he has tiny T-rex arms that cannot quite reach it.

Steve: 'Can you go get the Savlon?'

Me: 'It's not a Savlon problem; it is a hospital job.'

Steve: 'I'm not going to hospital. You're the nurse; you can work it out surely.'

Me: 'I'm not a doctor though, am I? Have you tried feeding it some salmon?'

Steve: 'You're not funny you know.'

Me: 'The six comedy awards in the lounge might disagree with you there. You need the hospital. They need to ultrasound it, like I had for the babies. Painless.

That is what you need. Or I could go to the shed, cobble together a GoPro on a snorkel and have a look inside myself. Your choice.'

He went to hospital. It was an abscess and a bit of something else fixable that I cannot remember the name of, all harmless in the scheme of things. He had an overnight stay that proved bountiful. He came home with two bollocks, newly diagnosed Atrial fibrillation (irregular heart), with a referral letter for sleep-apnoea investigations. One of his bollocks had a wound that required daily repacking with seaweed. His wound was 2-cm deep, so smaller than a grape. If you were to ask him, he would tell you it was as big as an orange. The oversized willy and the tiny arms can really mess with his perception of size.

On discharge he was also given a pamphlet that said he could relax for two weeks. Funny. You know, over the years doctors have told him to stop smoking, drink less and move more. He has never managed any of it. A doctor tells him to do naff-all for a fortnight and he bloody nails it. I had to remind him at times that our two children (both roughly the size of prize-winning marrows) exploded out of my vagina and I never got that pamphlet. At best, I was found crying on a park bench by an elderly woman who sat with me a while and suggested I sleep when they did.

Steve and I can bicker over how to stack a dishwasher and I was not about to have that level of tension while stacking his scrotum. I got the District nurses to pop out. I think Steve was secretly hoping for a gentle, beautiful nurse to make the whole thing a little less harrowing. Unfortunately for him, although District nurses are wonderful, big-hearted humans, most look like woodland creatures. But it turned out Steve's nurse was absolutely stunning to look at. I could not take my eyes off him. Steve and I miss Nurse James's visits very much.

This may have been a difficult read for any young man, with your hyper-sensitive, tight plums. You may whinge about the sensitivity of them now but one day you will miss it. Honestly, by the time you get to 70, those plums will be low-hanging fruit that someone could hit with a hammer and you would not bat an eyelid. We had an old bloke brought in by ambulance once. He was trapped in his plastic garden chair. He had sat down on it naked to shower and the warm water had melted his balls through the slats. He sat in triage, still in his chair, wrapped in blankets, his still damp head peering out of the top. By the look on his face, you would not have thought there was anything wrong at all. Turns out, he did not even notice himself until he tried to put his trousers on and he hit a snag.

If you are a young, virile man, by all means take pictures of your genitals, just do not send them to people. Keep them to yourself as something to remember him by when he is not what he once was. If you are someone who does not like their own penis, try to make friends with it. All penises are pretty much the same. I should know, I have seen thousands. They are also all different. I know because the 'growing-up' book I bought my boys had a page in it titled 'All penises are different' and had about 12 cartoon drawings of some of the variations on a theme. I used to take the book on the primary school pickup and sneak up on my candle-consultant mate's car and slap the book open on that page on her windscreen to surprise her. All fun and games till you get the wrong car.

# EIGHTEEN

# SURGICAL UNIT

### SLICE 'EM 'N' DICE 'EM.

have never worked in the private system. I am far too clumsy to work with body fluids around nice carpets and soft furnishings. Public health all the way for me, unless of course I am a patient. Well, you would go private if you could, wouldn't you? The public system does the best job it can with what it has but it does not get much and there is always a small chance you will be room sharing the pan room with a psychotic person.

Here are some little differences I noticed between the public and the private hospitals.

+ Private hospitals have Coco Pops. They only have the little 35g bags but you can ask for a few.

✚ They have a wine list. This would not work in the public system. We are already busy enough policing the pharmacy. Hospitals are open 24/7; if they provided alcohol the casino would have the hospitals closed for sure.

✚ You can have as many pillows as you want and you do not have to wrestle a paramedic for one. Yes, the public system has pillows, ones that we hide in cupboards awaiting bony or slumped admissions. When I was in a private hospital, I kept asking for pillows to see when they would run out and they did not. They wondered what I was doing with them. I got my husband to sneak them out in bin liners and I took them back to the public system.

I have thrice been an inpatient. My hospitalisations were planned and had a predicted path of recovery that would provide permeant relief from some moderate suffering. These types of hospitalisations are well . . . one might say I find them enjoyable. I love the prehospital bit; getting my ducks in a row in preparation for convalescence, the condensed health kick to optimise my organs, the new pyjamas and knickers shop. I adore the 12-hour post-operative dream fuzz, the heaviness of the body, the weightlessness of the mind. I savour the slowness of the recovery days, the fruit in jelly, the take-a-break puzzles.

I think I would never leave if I were not pushed, and I question if I prefer being a patient to being a nurse.

For many, hospitals are not as heavenly. Things can be unpredictable, irrevocable, incomprehensible or unknown. Much of a patient's day is spent thirsty, yes for fluids but also for relief, progress, company, orientation and answers. I have always viewed the morning wash round as a simple kindness in that day. I have given thousands of bed baths over the years. I have become very good at them. It is a part of the job I enjoy. A time to build trust and find out who the person in the bed is, and what they are thirsty for.

One of the first people I ever showered was ancient and skeletal. I adore wrinkles and she was covered in them. She was one part bones to four parts skin and it was hard to position her on the padded shower chair with its toileting hole in the middle. No matter how you sat her, you felt that if you turned away for a second her bones would slip through the hole leaving just the skin in the chair. I was instructed by my supervising registered nurse to shower her and to not forget the gum boots. I stripped the old dear down and before starting the shower I put the gum boots on . . . her. My intentions were good. I thought of the boots as a kind of foot spa, perhaps promoting circulation to the legs. I had not realised they were for me, to keep my work shoes dry. The gum boots filled with water, pinning the lady to the floor;

no risk of slipping in the shower if you cannot move your feet. The patient loved it, she wanted to keep the boots on – they made the stairs assessment difficult, but she had quads and hammies to die for by discharge.

I was ridiculed fondly and relentlessly for the rest of my placement, and it was a mistake you only make once. What it lacked in skill it made up for in creativity. I had my first bed bath at 42 years of age. This is when I found out that the kindness level very much depends on who is dishing it out.

I learned something about myself during the bed bath; I learned I was a three-person roll. That is, it takes three people to roll me over instead of the normal two people. I am aware I am medically fat, but it is not something I give much thought to. It is very hard to feel bad about your shape as a nurse; it is like the opposite of flicking through *Cosmopolitan* every day and feeling bad about yourself. If you see 15 or so of your average Joes in the nude each week, you tend to think you are doing all right. Many weeks I rank in the top 10.

I wanted a nice young nurse to do my bed bath. I hoped a dolphin would skip in with a sing song, 'Morning! Are you ready for your wash, Mrs Carroll? OH, sorry, I will come back later when you have finished your Coco Pops and your wine.' I did not get squeaky dolphin. The nurse I got was difficult to place chronologically. She was wide mouthed, lumpy, bad backed and twig legged, she had eyeballs so bulbous it made me want to massage her thyroid through her many chins to see if the eyes would pop back in again. Neither penguin nor orca, more toad, let us call her Sister Toad for confidentiality. I am not implying for a second that being attractive is a prerequisite to caring for others. Empathy and emotional intelligence have no physical qualities. Indeed, many of the people that save your life look like characters whom Pixar cut from *Monsters, Inc.* for being too scary for children.

I knew Sister Toad before I met her. She flicked on all the lights at 6.45 am when she arrived for her early shift. That tells you a lot about a person. She was the one who let me know I was a three-person roll. The way I found out was the worst bit. She opened the door and stuck her head in, eyeballs first, looked me up and down and shouted down the corridor, 'I am going to need more hands for this one.' As part of a profession that prides itself on breaking bad news gently, she ought to be ashamed of herself.

It was not so much a bed bath as an assault. She washed under my breast; I have always thought of that as just for special occasions, or sometimes they may just get a stealth cleaning if they float in the bath. She hiked the whole tit up by the nipple, with her teeth! There are only two parts of the flesh that the cloth should scrub rather than wipe, and they are the armpits and the soles of feet because they are too ticklish not to. Sister Toad was not of the same opinion. She went in for my delicate flower. Now fanny washing is not a taught skill, you develop your own methods, but here is mine. Feel free to borrow it should you ever need to.

## ONE GOOD WAY TO WASH FANNY

### Ingredients

Warm water (no soap, fannies should smell of fanny not Dettol™)

Cloth (not to be used elsewhere)

No talcum powder (else the environment down there turns it into a cement)

A person who needs a wash and is unable to get to their own fanny. (I could get to mine; I had had a leg operation. She only needed to ask me to put the wine down and I could have done my own.)

### Method

+ Let the person know what is about to happen.

+ Gain access to the affected area. If access is denied, it still needs a wash so do your best and try not to lose your hand.

+ Fluff the flaps out a little, squeeze wet flannel over it. Think Jamie Oliver squeezing lemons on salad leaves.

✚ Wet flannel again before you go in and swoosh it.

✚ Pat only the outside dry.

Not the method Sister Toad used. No words, no warning, just straight in there with the scourer scrubbing away like she was trying to get dried Weet-Bix off a bowl. She found bits of it that I never knew I had. Yes, it was clean job done, but I had to learn to walk again after it. It did not even need a wash; it had been washed just 24 hours prior and had done no work since. Essentially, they are self-cleaning. I took it on a four-day camping trip and it did not so much look at a flannel and it was fine.

It was very hard to stay mad at Sister Toad as she hopped about the unit feeding, watering, mobilising, transfusing, removing, measuring, highlighting, paging and inserting all in the same comprehensive manner. You need that kind of gun on short-stay surgical where the job is to get them up and out. Thanks to Sister Toad, I made superb progress on day two, showering independently rather than risk another genital mutilation.

I, myself, hate routine tasks to the point that when the GP gave me the contraceptive pill to take daily at 16 years old, I just used to take them all on a Friday because that is when I remembered I was going to get a shag. I got a lot of attention despite the 5 o'clock shadow that the pill gave me. In nursing, as in the rest of life, there are tasks so repetitive and mundane that it is hard to remember that they have a significance to the recipient. So just remember, should you ever be called upon to wash other peoples' fannies on repeat for decades, to keep it kind. It may be your millionth, but it's their one and only.

# NINETEEN

## ON THE DISTRICT

OFF-ROAD NURSING.

There were barriers between a nurse giving and Maud receiving care. The main one being that she was a bitter, lonely, awkward character. She managed her social calendar by requesting then rejecting care. Her only visitors were health professionals and she would make their visits last as long possible for respite from herself.

Maud would regularly summon paramedics only to spend a long time refusing to go to hospital. She would not have looked out of place in a hospital bed on any given day as she had end-stage everything. Her organs were ready to topple each other like dominoes; it would just take one hot day to kick off the kidneys and trigger the end. There was no documented mental-health diagnosis, but hoarding and top-shelf self-neglect indicated this was an oversight. This is not to say Maud was not a proud woman; in fact her pride caused most of her problems.

We visited Maud in the community as part of the District nurse patient load. She took an eternity to answer the door. Her decaying front door had several locks and deadbolts on the inside. She would take a while to acknowledge the knocking nurse before she stumbled and grumbled around the four-room unit hunting down the keys for each lock then fumble with each lock and wrong key before completing her mission. It took forever to get into her house and nurses are simply not built for standing still.

It was hard not to be in a bad mood by the time you entered but I would pass the time by imagining Maud was an escapologist darting around the tank filled with water against the clock, a graceful sequined flipper replacing her gargantuan leaky legs. In both reality and fiction, Maud knew exactly where the keys were and how they worked, only in fiction was she against the clock. Once the main door was open, you were only nearly there. She would fuck about with the snib on the ripped fly-screen door for a bit. She was a master of her art.

They sent one nurse out to dress Maud's enormous, exploded legs. The soggy nappies and crepe bandages were removed and replaced daily without any real hope of healing. There was more saturated padding and raw leg than one nurse could handle. It would have been better to send three or four so they could take a bandage each and dance around her calves like a maypole.

She would heckle as you worked. She once said to a student tending to her, 'If I'd been a spinster at your age with a face as plain as yours, I would have got a better hairdresser.' Maud had had four husbands, which explains quite a lot. Four husbands could make a woman grumpy.

It was a roasting Adelaide day when Maud stopped answering the door altogether. Not only did she not answer the door, there was a horrific smell coming from the house. She had to be in there because she never went out, and I doubt she was invited to parties. Given the heatwave we were in, it was likely that her kidneys had shrivelled, her blood pressure had plummeted, her potassium had stockpiled and her heart had stopped.

If you are worried someone has died at home, the policy is to phone the police to break in and check. As she was presumed dead, I said a little word to whoever for her. If there were indeed pearly gates, I suggested Saint Peter take ages looking for the keys to it before he let her in. She would love that.

The police were excellent as always. They took a fraction of the time Maud did to open the door. An officer and I worked through the stench to get to the bedroom and found Maud slumped up in bed lifeless and glassy-eyed, sat in a pool of sick and diarrhea. The police officer stood in the doorway with his hand over his mouth and nose.

As a nurse, I do not have the power to certify someone as dead, but I do a solid job of checking for signs of life. Having not recently read the 'Are they dead or just pretending?' policy, I defaulted to what I thought should probably happen. I went in to feel the carotid pulse but to be honest there was too much vomit on the jowl to be sure. She still felt warm though and did not yet have the waxy look of the dead, so I did the old shoulder shake.

She blinked.

Now for the nonmedical people, dead people do not blink. You must be alive for that to happen. She blinked and she spoke, so she was definitely alive but having quite the dreadful day.

Maud: 'I've shat the bed. I need cordial.'

You have never seen a police officer shoot off quite so quickly.

Maud: 'I've shat the bed; you'll have to clean me up.'

Me: 'I am here to dress your legs. I do not have the stuff I need for a shit-the-bed situation. We have known each other a few years now. I would even say we are friends. I would not leave a friend in a mess like this. I will help you but as friends, I am going to need some manners.'

She sat silent in her shit for a while weighing up her options.

Maud: 'I have shat the bed . . . I need cordial . . . please.'

I took that as a win. She was able to sit and shower as I changed the bedding. I laid out the dressings I would need after she climbed back into bed. I contacted a friend to collect my children from school as I would be running late.

Me: 'How nice is that? All sorted now, just the dressings and I will be out of here.'

Maud: 'I still need cordial.'

There was a stand-off again, but I got another please. Who says you cannot teach an old dog new tricks? When I returned with the drink, the main part of the dressing, the nappies, were not visible. I put the drink on the bedside table.

Me: 'Maud. Where are the dressings?'

Maud: 'Under the bed. They fell.'

I was close to crying; the old dog had indeed taught herself a new trick. This was not a floor you wanted to crawl on or a bed you wanted to be under given recent events. I steeled myself for going under. I had to get my arms, shoulders and head under the bed to reach where she had thrown them. They had not fallen. I crawled in and grabbed the nappy and started to work my way out as quickly as possible. I felt a stab in the back of my neck from the bed frame and I realised I had become impaled on a rogue nail sticking inwards from the bedframe.

I told Maud what had happened from my position.

That I was nailed to the frame just under the base of my skull. I asked her to get help from the locksmith the police had sent to fix the door. It was like she could not hear me.

It was dark under the bed; I had a pen torch in my pocket. I decided to not use it to look around. I was worried I might see the heads of four ex-husbands nailed to the frame too. There was nothing for it; I just had to rip my neck off the nail. I did it, and the pain was the kind of pain that shoots down the back of your leg and makes you queasy no matter where it originates.

I stood up and after putting a dressing on my own neck, I dressed her legs with no eye contact, fighting frustrated tears and in near-complete silence. I spoke once only to say that I would need a tetanus shot and that I was bleeding. She responded, but only to point out that cordial should come with a straw and that it was too weak. I had not realised I was making it for Gordon Ramsay. Good of her to drink it at ALL really.

I held the tears until I got outside. I might not have cried at all had the locksmith not asked if I was OK. We sat on a wall and I told him the whole story, trying to maintain confidentiality by not mentioning names, which seems a little pointless as he knew exactly which house I had come out of. He had been in it as I walked out. I talked about the frustrations of looking after the awkward and ungrateful, about delay tactics and mean comments making a day's work harder. Visits to Maud became much quicker after this one. She had learned nothing, but the door now had only one deadbolt.

Nursing on the district, you begin to realise that there are many ways that a person can open a door. Sometimes like Maud, it is almost as if they have never opened a door before. Other times they are sat right behind the screen door lurking in the dark ready to scare the living daylights out of you. The amount of people who do not wear pants to answer the door is astounding. A pantless greeting is an almost exclusively male pastime. I understand that I am nurse and that I have seen it all before, but they do not know that this particular knock is the nurse. It could be Jehovah's Witnesses or the *Sunrise* Cash Cow. I was once accosted by a panicked gentleman at the door with no pants or underpants on. His urine catheter was giving him a lot of discomfort, and he was visibly pained.

'Thank God you are here,' he said. 'This catheter is going to be the death of me. You know anything about them?'

'I know a bit. Let's get you to the bedroom and I will have you sorted,' I said.

Five minutes later, he was laid out on the bed recovering, still pantless. I had done a bit of manipulating and sorted him, as promised.

'Thanks for that, I couldn't possibly have waited for the nurse,' he said.

'Who do you think I am?' I said.

'Are you not the Avon lady with my wife's delivery?' he said.

Some houses are full of people and feel empty, other houses are full of life with just one person in them. Nat was a patient whose house was somehow bursting with life with just a cruise FM on the wireless, her beloved back-in-the-day drama series *Heartbeat*, a gallery wall of her Jimmys (My Jimmy, Big Jimmy, Little Jimmy, Prison Jimmy, Jimmy and Jimmy getting married, Jimmy the Jive . . .) and her squidgy, gorgeous, Scottish self. Visits would always take place at a kitchen table set for two, always with two homemade crocheted doily place settings. As the widow and matriarch of a pack of Jimmies, many of whom I had met over the years, she must have had more than the odd adversity but in the eight years I had seen her in and out of hospital, I had only ever seen her be anything but joyful one time. There was nothing sadder than a flat Nat, no one wants that, so I stayed for a chat.

Me: 'What is it, Nat?'

Nat: 'Baby Daniel died last night.'

Me: 'Oh my goodness, I'm so sorry, Nat.'

Nat: 'I feel so stupid. I can normally get past this sort of thing. I dunno, the wee bairn only got two days. He was a wee premmie. So tiny, so little, she never got to even hold him. Two days! I got 83 years and I still don't want to go. Two days. Don't worry yourself, go on, do what you need to do. I'll see myself right.'

I had to take blood, but sticking pins in a grieving woman did not seem right. I went and made her a sugary cuppa first and let her talk. Apparently, Gina, Daniel's mother, had broken up a fight in the pub and got hit in the stomach which sent her into labour. Such senseless violence. So many lives forever changed. This was dreadful.

Me: 'Have you got one of the Jimmys coming to sit with you?'

Nat: 'Yeah, Jimmy Jugs is coming round later. He'll put me right.'

Me: 'So when did all this happen?'

Nat: 'Last night.'

Me: 'Give yourself a bit of time, Nat. This is huge, so senseless. Give yourself till after the funeral at least.'

Nat: 'Yes, I suppose. It's next Wednesday.'

Me: 'They organised that quickly.'

Nat: 'It's every Wednesday; it's always Wednesdays.'

Me: 'Nat . . . who is baby Daniel?'

Nat: 'Baby Daniel from *Heartbeat*, Gina's baby. Oh my! Did you think I was upset over a real baby, Oh my, [laughing] I'm so sorry?'

Me: 'Nat, you got upset over a TV baby? Belt up, woman, you are 84. Two of your real friends have probably died this morning.'

Nat gave me a big roar; she was still laughing about it at the next visit.

'You really pulled me out of the glums. I'd like you to have this,' she said.

I am now the proud owner of a doily placemat, a Nat original. You would wonder what use a singular non-wipeable placemat would be for a family woman like myself who misses her mouth on the regular. I refused at first. I asked what she would use if a Jimmy wanted to stay for tea.

'A little snippet of wisdom for the future. When you are old, like me, don't make visitors too comfortable. That way if they want you for any more than tea and scones, they have to take you somewhere fancy.'

Nurses are not allowed to accept gifts. I suppose it makes sense, as I would totally give you more painkillers if you were to buy me a PlayStation or an electric bike. I accepted that placemat because there is nothing I would not do for Nat even if I was not paid in quirky table wear. I took it as part of the Nursing rewards program. Nursing has gifted me many things over the years. Not all the gifts are wanted, like Plantar fasciitis, oste-oarthritis, a torn rotator cuff and being colonised with golden staph. Some of the gifts make your heart sing even though they are truly awful, and I treasure those as some would cherish a Mother's Day pasta necklace gift. Some people just love to give and it would offend to refuse.

I remember a gorgeous little bedridden dot of an oldie who used to wrap her bedside trinkets in toilet roll as thankyous. Giving her stuff away would bring her such joy that you would always accept it just to see her smile. She had memory loss so we would slip the trinkets back onto her bedside table overnight only to receive it back again wrapped in toilet roll the next day.

Apart from the placemat, there is one other gift I treasure. Here is how it came into my possession. It was the final visit to a house we had spent a lot of time in, the Mrs of the house had needed 30-minute antibiotic infusions daily for a couple of months and no longer required them. The Mr had been proud to tell me that him and Mrs had gotten me a little something to show their appreciation for all the excellent care I had taken with the Mrs. There was not a lot of work to be done once in the house, but you did have to make small talk for the half-hour and the couple were ditherers and would take forever to get in position and then struggle to find a letter they needed you to look at after the infusion ended. The Mr in particular was a noisy and excruciatingly slow riser from a chair. Once on the move, you were never really sure he had gotten out of the chair because he held himself so crookedly. You have to love a tryer but if my husband ever moves that slowly he is going in a home.

Mr: 'It's here somewhere.'

Me and Mrs sat and watched all eight Harry Potters

back-to-back together while he riffled around in bedrooms trying to find the gift. *This present had better be spectacular,* I thought. And it did not disappoint.

He was proud as punch as he handed me the gift: an A4 piece of paper with a ye olde map print of a Northern English county on it.

'That's lovely. A vintage map of the Yorkshire,' I said.

'Yes, it's a photocopy of that tea towel you said you liked, of your home county.'

I honestly don't remember ever saying I liked a tea towel in my life. You make a lot of chatter in a slow couple's house and you don't always remember it all. I was not from Yorkshire, and they were not from Yorkshire either. One of their friends had been there and bought it back for them, and they had always wanted to go there. That was an achievable goal missed in my opinion. I would not suggest Mr and Mrs try it now, 80 years around the world would not be long enough.

'I did, I did love that tea towel. I have never had anything quite like it. Nothing, but nothing, says thank you like the photocopy of a tea towel.' (Except maybe the actual tea towel.) 'I had no idea you had a photocopier back there.'

'I don't.' Prouder still, he was almost stood upright at this point. 'I took the tea towel to a shop called Officeworks.'

I cannot begin to fathom how long that journey must

have taken. If Harry Potter managed to split his high-school years into eight films, Mr going to Officeworks with a tea towel would be a 10-parter, the first three would be him trying to get out of the chair.

'Can I give you some money for it? Printing is not cheap.'

'It wasn't. It was going to be $4.95 if I had it printed and made smaller, but the girl in the shop and I worked out that if she made copies of it in four sections and shrunk each section and cut them out and she sticky-taped them back together, it would be $4.50. She didn't charge me anything for the sticky tape or labour. I told her I wanted it so you could frame it.'

'And THAT, that is definitely what I will be doing. Pride of place this one.'

It is a gift that keeps on giving. I smile whenever I look at it. I believe it is a gift that changed someone's life. I reckon the day Mr eventually got to Officeworks and asked a girl to photocopy a tea towel, in quarters, then to trim all four down and cut them out and tape them back together was the very same day that young girl went home from Officeworks and said to her parents, 'I think I am ready to go to university now.'

The privilege of working with someone in their home is that people are more themselves. They are letting you into their world and trusting you. It is a real honour to see what people have made of their lives. Sometimes you walk in a house and think to yourself, *OK, someone really loves peacocks.* They sit at their peacock tablecloth, drinking from their peacock mugs, doing a crystal art of a peacock. It is another piece of a person that you get to enjoy. You do think to yourself, *If you people love peacocks so much, why have you not bought an actual peacock at some point?* Get yourself on Facebook Marketplace; there are millions of them. It is a very achievable dream and surely less labour intensive than crystal art.

Getting to know strangers so intimately in their own habitat has taught me that on the most part people get to choose to be happy, or not. You can be like Nat who, despite having suffered the tragic loss of a much-loved imaginary baby who only pretend died, still found a way to laugh. You can be like Maud and lock yourself away. You can be happy and content without having everything you ever wanted, like the peacock people. Or you can be completely fulfilled by not wearing trousers around your castle and letting the Avon lady mess with you for relief. However you do it, just be sure to remember the choice is yours and it is a choice worth making.

# TWENTY

# CENTRAL
# CONTROL UNIT

## WHO IS IN CHARGE AROUND HERE?

On 11 September 2001, the planes hit the towers as I slept in the middle of a night shift roster. I saw the footage when I woke up for my midday wee. I phoned the boss and said that I would not be in to work that night because World War Three had started and the world was ending. The boss said, 'It may well be, but you still have to come in.' There is an unstoppable force to healthcare that halts for nothing and no one.

All the special days are movable. They have to be, as there is always something more pressing inside the hospital walls than there is in a singular life or events outside of it. You need the right number of staff inside the hospital, of the right skill level. There is no getting away from it. To make a point, amidst the barbary of war, international etiquette and ethics have been agreed upon in the Geneva Convention. It is forbidden to kill medical staff on either team, which seems reasonable. It is fair game, however, to kidnap them from the enemy if you are short-staffed on your side. I love this idea; it is much needed in the public system. Next time someone phones in sick leaving our ward short, I shall just nip to a neighbouring ward, club a penguin, whack a pillowcase over its head and drag it back to our unit. If the kidnapped penguin wakes up grumpy, I will just tell them Geneva told me to do it.

To ensure the hospital has the right balance of people power and skill set inside, all staff must become submissive to the roster monkeys. Roster monkeys live two months in the future, nesting in paperwork, obsessing over skill mix, drowning in coffee and requests for social-calendar clemency. Because the roster monkeys are from the future, they need to know you really want or need the day/night off eight weeks before you know that you want it off. I have never been a roster monkey. I have chosen instead to be paid a teensy bit less and have people like me.

It takes a short while to acclimatise to being the hospital's bitch, but there are up sides if you are crafty about it. I can go shopping mid-week when the shops are quiet and I can get drunk on a Tuesday because technically it is a weekend. I never have to miss a school assembly although school assemblies are a waste of a roster request after Year 4. The first few years are too cute to miss. Some of the little squibs look like they fell out of the womb onto the plastic gym mats just this morning and when they find their little balls and start belting out stuttered monotone facts down the mic my heart could just about burst. But really after Year 4, I gave myself permission to sit at home watching *Judge Judy* and scratching nuts. You can make your kids think you went by asking somebody who did go what happened and then disseminate that info to your kid in the car so they think you went. If your children really wanted you to come, they would up the production level. Like would the odd aerial entry and a few pyrotechnics kill them? Well it might, but it might be worth it. And while we are at it, EDIT. I don't need a collage, an acrostic poem AND a song about how milk comes from cows. We adults already know that bit, so why not teach us something new? Parents be sat at the back googling cockroach milk while kids be doing *Cow Tits: the musical* at the front.

As the Gregorian calendar chugs along, the hospital buggers with it. The special national celebration days have a temper to them that is at odds with the outside world and commercial image. Front of house is like the world flipped inside out. On Valentine's Day, the waiting rooms and gurneys are full of lonely hearts. Come Christmas, the beds are full of people alone and fasting.

The gall stones and pancreatitis sufferers do not attend, instead they chow down on antacids, baste in goose fat and pickle the pancreas so as not to ruin a family day. They ruin their new year instead.

We mark these special days in the staffrooms and nurses' stations. We bring in share food and wear silly hats and scrubs. Everything we pop into patients has its expiry date checked by a nurse, sometimes two. The date-checking of food in the staffroom spread does happen but in a much more relaxed fashion. If you walk in any staffroom over Christmas and New Year there will be food on the table, you do not know how long it has been there and there are that many different wonderful cultures working together to heal people that, quite often, you do not know what you are eating. It may look like a cake yet taste like a curry, it may look like nasi goreng but taste like Turkish delight. It is truly a joy for a glutton like myself. Blessed are the bakers, for they shall not be workplace bullied. Anyway, this is how you date check staffroom food.

> **Nurse 1:** 'Does anyone know how long this food has been out?'
> **Nurse 2:** 'Well, I finished an early on Tuesday and it was not there then.'
> **Nurse 1:** 'OK, what day is it now?'
> **Nurse 2:** 'I have no idea.'

**Nurse 1:** 'OK, let's just eat it and see what happens, we are in a hospital if it goes wrong.'

Like medication, it still takes two nurses to check but it is not quite as safe. It may surprise you that given the risks, there is no policy about staffroom buffets, yet management have found time to make a policy about when and what Christmas scrubs are permitted. I think it is called the 'pissing on the festive joy policy'.

Political campaigns and news outlets often quantify the integrity of a healthcare system in terms of shiny new hospitals and more new beds. What they often forget is that even if the hospitals and the beds cease to be a thing, the staff that power it still have to function, often more so. We could do what we do in a broom cupboard, or a corridor, or in a queue of ambulances outside the hospital, and we often do.

A Cairns hospital closed temporarily in 2011, as it was in the path of Cyclone Yasi. The hospital shut, and the patients were evacuated to other hospitals. Nurse Katie East and her team ploughed on and threw together a makeshift care facility on a basketball court. Hurricanes and cyclones are believed to send pregnant women into labour en masse. There are many papers that dispute this but two babies were brought into the world simultaneously on that court separated by only a pegged-up hospital sheet. *SWISH!*

Again, Lebanon was decimated in 2020 when a storage facility of ammonium nitrate exploded, causing catastrophic devastation. When the blast happened, Pamela, a NICU nurse, was working on the second floor of Saint George's Hospital, where the windows and walls blew in, covering the prem babies' incubators in the blood of her colleagues and rubble. Pamela grabbed three prem babies in her arms and ran three miles to the nearest incubator. She took clothes from passersby to keep the babies warm. Two of the three babies were from a set of triplets, their sibling already well and discharged. All the rescued babies lived. I am not crying; you are crying.

Bravery like this comes in many different forms. At the very end of my studentship, it was the turn of the century. Prince instructed me to party like it was 1999 and the NHS was not going to stop that. I was prepared to be hit by a truck rather than work late or on the night of NYE, or worse still, be rostered early the morning after. To get out of working, the plan was for me to lie on a concrete driveway and have my brother drive over my arm with his mate's work van. The dress code was formal wear (for the party of the millennium, not the car accident). I had bought a sleeveless gown to accommodate the plaster cast, and a matching shawl to fashion into a sling. Not all heroes wear capes; some of us wear shawls.

✚

To say that a shift worker's calendar is cluttered would be an understatement; the next-level organisation you need to coordinate hospital time with real-world time is insane. It is inevitable that things will be missed and so the non-shift worker friend or family member, who is often let down by a nurse at the last moment for other commitments, may find the nurse to be quite flakey. They would be wrong, what they are actually witnessing is organised chaos bordering on genius, as the next story will show. I had two children under four with a nine-to-five husband and my friend Helen had four under five and no partner. He had run off, having decided family was not for him.

I don't blame him, four is a lot. Helen blames him a little bit, more so after wine. Helen and I would work the same night shifts where possible so we could co-snooze and still parent the six children in the day as sister wives. Dealing with all six pre-schoolers together was way easier than handling my two warring toddler siblings alone, so Helen and I both got something out of the arrangement. It all sounds quite neglectful, snoozing while six slapstick, free-range pre-schoolers scuttled around dropping snacks on the floor (it is easier to vac than cook). We kicked in when necessary, usually to parent middle child of the tribe, Helen's Jacob, to free a head wedged in a baby gate, or to un-paint a dog.

A great hack for wearing little ones out with minimal

effort on the adults' part is a game we called electric fence. Helen and I would lie on the floor and the children would use us as an assault course. There is something soporific about having babies crawling over you when you are sleepy, like a slobbery massage with the mini-masseuse prizing your eyelid open every now and again to see if you are still there. The electric part for all of us was when we woke up a bit and squeezed and tickled them all and they tried to wriggle away. It was a game of intense suspense for the babies but very little effort on our part.

The oldest child, the director of the impromptu kindy, was Becka. She was the only one who could clear jump over us without getting electrocuted.

One day we heard her lining up her minions, barking orders. 'If you jump over *my* mummy without touching the fence, you get five points. If you can clear jump over Aunty Georgie, you get a billion points.' Thanks for the heckle, Becka. Becka even parented us adults some night rosters. If Helen or I got overtired and weepy, she would bring us a cup of invisible tea and some plastic broccoli from the play kitchen, cover us in blankets and stick *Jurassic Park* on for us. Bless you, child. Helen and I would sit quietly while all the rest of Becka's brood ran amuck. Not surprisingly, Becka is now a registered nurse on a stroke unit and incredible at it.

All those times were over a decade ago and I look back

and cannot begin to fathom how Helen was the executive function for four busy, tiny but ever-growing bodies and brains at home then she went to work and did the same for adults in crisis. Both her home and work were hurtling along 24/7. Helen was a true wonder woman back then and a phone call from her a short while back reminded me of how flawless she still is.

Helen: 'So Jacob's 17 now, sort of, anyway.'

Me: 'Oh my goodness, how's he going? They grow up quick.'

Helen: 'Some days are quicker than others. I told him to grow up the other day. What are you going to do after puberty, I says. Adultery, he says. Puberty! Adultery! My idiot boy. I mean, statistically he is correct, if not grammatically. Anyway, you are never going to believe this. So it's Jacob's birthday, and he wants driving lessons. I know you always say it takes a village, so I asked the sperm donor if he could chip in, but apparently his new family need braces so he's a bit short. As much use as a barbed-wire speculum, that fella. Turns out, I am "the village". So, Jacob wants the driving lessons, needs a driver's permit, needs ID to get the permit, needs a birth certificate. But I can't find it anywhere. It's just . . . not . . . anywhere!'

Me: 'Have you asked Becka?'

Helen: 'She couldn't find it either.'

Understandably, like all the best houses, Helen's house was chaos.

Me: 'Well, it's gone then.'

Helen: 'So, I go to the registry office to get a copy. Jacob Humphrey Shiphard. Born at Rochdale Infirmary, 8/3/2003. Father, Padraig Shiphard. Even they couldn't find it. *Can you spell the name again . . . sorry again, . . . again, are you sure that's correct?* Yep, I know what my son's called. *And the father's name, could you spell that again . . . and again, P . . . A . . . D . . . what?* That bloody man. I've spent more time spelling out and respelling his name than he spent inside me at this point. *Are you sure he was born at Rochdale Infirmary?* OOH, let me think, yes I am. I think if memory serves me well, I'm pretty sure I was at the start of the labour and I'm sure as hell I was there at the end of it too. I'm all like, "Well, you better find it."'

Me: 'Sounds like you told her. So have you got it now?'

Helen: 'Yes, here's the thing, she called me in for it. Turns out the names and birthplace were all correct.'

Me: 'Go you.'

Helen: '. . . It was the date of birth that was wrong.'

Me: 'How have they managed that?'

Helen: 'Georgie, . . . *they* had it right! . . . *I* had it wrong! We have been celebrating Jacob's birthday on the wrong day for I don't know how many years. I don't know when it started. Surely I got the first few right. It's the first of March, NOT the eighth. Primary-school years were busy. We always moved special days to fit the roster and I reckon one year I just transferred it over wrong in the new diary. Mum says she always thought it was wrong but didn't want to question me because I "looked like I had enough on my plate".'

Me: 'You utter fuck knuckle, that's priceless. Don't forget you did an awful lot right too. How's he taken it?'

Helen: 'He asked for two cakes, one on the first and one the eighth every year from now on as dickhead tax. I reckon he deserves that. It will all get eaten. I've had to buy three this year. Had to take one in to the woman at the registry office too.'

# TWENTY-ONE

## RECOVERY

**WE SHALL REBUILD IT, BIGGER AND
STRONGER THAN EVER.**

**M**y mother's partner Norman had a bloody death without any real battle on his part. He had retired in his thirties so that he could listen to old records, win pub quizzes and tinker with things. He had predicted for himself a youngish death and attributed this belief to having been orphaned in his boyhood, both parents being eaten by cancers. What he felt he had learned from his own parents' deaths was that for him cancer was inevitable. The cancer did not kill you, he thought. The doctors prodding it did. He did not mind dying but he did not want it to be painful. Even before his own cancer diagnosis, it was as if he had begun to self-palliate with baked cheesecake, vodka orange and *Antiques Roadshow*. He very much spent his whole adult life fulfilling his simple bucket list as a result. Well done, Norm.

I do not exactly remember where his cancer started but after three years of surgeries and infusions, it ended up everywhere. Norman was aware that he was dying. He had definitive signs that his body was failing: jaundice, swelling, loss of appetite, chest pains. He was attuned to what dying looks like as a child. My mum, on the other hand, had not thought about him dying. If her brain did occasionally break ranks and ponder Norm's passing, their last few days together would have involved some gentle drifting, hand holding, and perhaps an impromptu wedding for the two of them. If you were to ask Mum how Norm was faring, she would keep things chipper and feed you a shit sandwich then give you a milkshake to wash it down.

> **Mum:** 'Norm is doing fantastic; we went to The Dolce Vita last night. I mean, he didn't eat anything but more for me, hey! Do you know though, Miguel behind the bar there, he's not even Italian, he just pretends when he's working?'
>
> Or . . .
>
> **Mum:** 'Norm is as strong as an ox. I mean, he gets chest pain but only if he moves, so long as we just do the Simpson Clough walk, and I help him up the steps bit, he does all right. Do you know what we noticed?

You never see white dog shit anymore, do you? Norm says it's to do with acid rain.'

Norman never had a comment about his disease progression, and I thank him for sparing my mum that impending doom. He filled conversation instead with rants about hospital parking and clinics that ran late, which was nearly as contentious for the pair of them. I got where he was coming from. I would absolutely fume about those wasted hours if I knew I was running out of time too. It turned out in the end that his belief that 'cancer don't kill people, doctors prodding do' was almost a self-fulfilling prophecy.

> **Mum:** 'He did really well. He had his teeth out today, so another box ticked. He's home now but there seems to be a lot of blood, Georgie. I've phoned the clinic and they said that it's normal and he should just bite on something. Anyway, have you seen? Anna Friel, the one we used to give a lift to theatre workshop with the birthmark, she's in a film with Anthony Hopkins now and the birthmark's gone.'

That was the start of the end. Norm had had his teeth removed for chemotherapy and started to haemorrhage from the cavities. There was nothing normal about this and he had no bite left in him. He slept and Mum changed the bloody towels under his head till later that night when he became combative. An ambulance took him to the local urgent-care centre where they were somewhat successful in stopping him dying. A patch-up job with plans to do more.

> **Mum:** 'He's asleep now thank goodness. I am furious at the hospital, furious. I am spitting. They let him self-discharge. I got a phone call from him not even them. He was out in the car park, wandering around in his pyjamas wanting picking up. I cannot believe they let him out, he's not bleeding but he's not better . . .'

She was now serving an open shit sandwich with no milkshake. He was readmitted to a larger hospital within 24 hours and over the following three days, Norman bled to death from the mouth; sedated, ventilated and on inotropic support medication that forced heart contractions. There really was nothing more that could be done, maximum life support was no longer supporting life.

> **Mum:** 'He's gone, he died, and I wasn't there. I keep looking for him. I keep thinking he is just in the next room.'

Waiter, it appears that there is no bread in my mother's sandwich, and there are maggots in the shite. Mum, I am so sorry this happened to you. The waiter said you just have to eat on or starve. It is never nice dining alone so come live with us in Australia for a bit while you chew it over.

Mum's grief locked on hard to the notion that Norm would still be alive if the dental surgeon had taken more care. If they had not let him self-discharge. If they had not wasted so much time asking over and over if he wanted resuscitating in the Emergency room. If they had just started transfusing blood the instant he was readmitted. If the nurse had not told her to go home and rest a bit, and if the big hospital not been so far away, she would have been at his side as he died. She was bitter and vocal about everything in her grief. Even my normally cherished family were demonised; my children were spoiled little bastards, my husband was an uncouth bully and I was far too fat.

In troubled times, most people tend to give up God and turn to the bottle or give up alcohol through finding the Lord but not my mum. She was both drunk and religious. She can do anything if she puts her mind to it. For a year, I listened to her venomously berating the hospital system I knew so well. I had had many years' experience on the ICU and I knew why they did the things they did and did not do the things they did not do. Mum had the experience I had never had. She had had someone she loved very much die 'unexpectedly' and graphically on Intensive Care. I knew from the inside we do not *let* people self-discharge; the 'self' bit means they choose to against medical advice. We are not kidnappers. They get paid more and have fewer workplace injuries. Asking someone with cancer of the everywhere and uncontrolled haemorrhage if they have any end-of-life plans is a perfectly reasonable question. We do not just start blood on leaky people because it would be as futile as pumping a slashed tyre with air. The nurse that convinced her to go home had certainly not done it to get her out of the way. They were caring for my mum as much as they were for Norman. I said none of these things. Instead I listened over wine and cheese on our front porch while trying not to displease her by getting any fatter.

Steve needed a break from the heckling, the children had begun avoiding Grandma and Mum now seemed too comfortable in her anger. So I decided to change things up a bit and take a road trip with the boys, Mum and Jesus (Jesus was always with her). It was to be a camping holiday travelling around the country towns of South Australia. Me, the kids, Grandma and Jesus. We are not a camping family; we had no equipment. We went to Kmart and bought a four-man tent, which we thought made perfect sense because there were four of us, none of us man-sized. The tent must have been tested by four Lego men because we spent the first night sleeping inside each other. It was not a total loss, as putting up the tent had been a breeze and we had loved the campfire.

After a night of no sleep, packing up the tent proved to be more than any of us could handle. The tent bag had definitely shrunk in the night. I tapped out quickly, declaring that there was more chance of me getting my then 10-year-old son back up my vagina than there was of repackaging that tent. Mum, however, would not give up even though it made her furious. The kids and I sat on a log next to the dying fire and waited for an end to the punching, sitting on, squashing and swearing. We got the giggles a couple of times at the ridiculousness of it. We would occasionally offer to help only to be told, 'I've nearly got it . . . FUCK STICKS!' The flapping eventually stopped, which just left Mum sat on a pile of canvas, bottom lip about to go. I got up off the log, stood over her and said, 'Let me help, you can't do this alone.' She passed me the tent and bag.

I made no attempt to repackage the equipment and instead maintained eye contact as I put both the bag and tent straight on to the fire. It was the first proper belly laugh I had heard from her since Norm had died and it was glorious. She surprised herself with it and burst into happy tears. Laughing and sobbing big, globby, snotty tears in the centre of a family hug as the tent burned.

We stayed in motels after that and it seemed the shitter the motel, the more fun we had. Mum talked less and less about the injustice of it all and the boys fell in love with her again. It became incredibly easy to make her laugh and it was so rewarding that it was impossible to resist trying.

The last stop was Mount Gambier. The four of us and Jesus sat around a table ploughing through pub grub instead of choking on shit sandwiches, all of us howling at the funny stuff that had happened. The tour guide of the (not at all blue unless you go view it in certain light at a certain time of year) Blue Lake who looked at the ceiling and spoke through his nose the whole time. Teaching the boys to drive on a salt plain. Making Grandma shout 'Nice arse' at a road runner as we passed him, then circling back to make her do it again only to lock the window down and drive at the same speed as the runner, instructing her to apologise to the nice man for her appalling manners.

The joy at our table sparked the attention of a gap-toothed bogan bar fly who took a shine to Mum and came over to flirt with her. Mum turned into an absolute pony, flipping her hair around and being all impressive. The boys gawped, wondering what the hell had happened to Grandma. I told them hormones had happened to Grandma. Jesus had definitely left the building.

Bogan decided he was taking Mum to the sinkhole for a date. He asked my permission. I said it depended on what a sinkhole was. He said it was like a hole . . . in the ground . . . but bigger. How could I not let my mum go enjoy that romantic evening?

'What do you think, boys, should we let Grandma go to a big hole with a stranger she met in a bar?'

The answer was a unanimous yes.

We waited up in the pub for Grandma and my new daddy to return, in case he did not bring her back and we had to go dig her out of the big hole. Turns out we need not have worried; the sinkhole is a magnificent botanised open-top cave. They came back holding hands as she told the boys and me that he took her there to feed the possum. Well, the kids and I had never heard 'it' called that before. It became a catchphrase for the rest of the road trip. Whatever the bogan did with her possum, we are all grateful, as it perked her right up.

# TWENTY-TWO

# GERONTICS / GERIATRICS

## WHERE ARE MY OLD CODGERS AT? IMMA COMIN' FOR YOU.

Old age is not for everyone. By that I mean, not everyone gets to savour it. Those who get to be old in years become old in soul at very different ages. The World Health Organisation (WHO) suggests that in the Western world, 60 is old. I feel that this number was picked by someone in their twenties. In truth, old age can come at any age, and it never arrives for some no matter how long they live. So just to cover all bases, let's start at the very beginning of the aging process and you just decide when your old is.

You can breed from any combination of fertile humans so long as there is sperm, eggs and alcohol involved. Fertility potential is activated during puberty. This is incredibly poor design given the pubescent child has the internet and no frontal cortex, the part of the brain that looks at long-term planning.

Given that fertility (or lack of) for women can go on for 30-ish years, sexually active adults are shagging either fretfully trying to conceive or fervently trying to avoid it. There is no rhyme or reason to how this works. Roughly 50 per cent of Australian pregnancies are unplanned. Reasons for falling pregnant can range from an over-whelming desire to create a life, an image in your likeness, right through to 'we did not think we could get pregnant if we did it stood up'.

Once the spoof and *oeff* get all mixed together, they might become a zygote. The man then sits on the fertil-ised zygote while the woman goes on holiday with all her mates in search of food. She returns to the egg in time to see the baby person peck its way painlessly out of its shell. Sorry, that's penguins. I always get that wrong.

Baby-carrying humans, on the other hand, tend to be women. They do not sit on the eggs; they carry them around in a bag on their insides while they work construc-tion jobs, nurse, go to the gym or become prime minister. Ideally, babies should be delivered headfirst out of the same hole the penis went up but can be breech meaning they come out feet, bottom or . . . wait for it . . . knees first. I just learned the knees thing and it is the single most disturbing medical fact in this book. The newborns burst out of the adult whenever they feel like it, dragging some of her insides outside, making the adult female shit the bed in front of her loved one. We have a lot to learn from penguins.

The sex of a human is assigned at birth: male, female, or intersex (m/f/x). There are privileges or hurdles given to all from the get-go: longed for and hard won, or unwanted by one or more of its makers. Contented or addicted. Healthy or medically fragile. Regardless, they are all blessings and babies are everything. They are all loved by someone, be that a social worker, hospital chaplain, midwife or the volunteers that knit tiny, tiny hats, cardigans and stuffed animals for them.

Babies are simultaneously helpless and fearless. They are equipped with teeny, tiny toes, chubby cheeks, button noses, massive eyes and piercing noises. These features combined makes them both difficult to ignore and impossible to say no to. They do not ask for much, but they are relentless and repetitive in their demands.

Babies have evolved over the millennia from hairy, robust, little sabre-tooth babies to the modern-day influencer infant that suffocates in the presents of peanuts, but breathes just fine if you plunge them underwater.

Next comes the toddler years. The toddler spends its days being either distraught or ecstatic. A toddler is a powerful thing; it can look you in the eye while crapping itself. It is brutally honest to strangers if something about them is different, yet can be a bare-faced liar about colouring on Grandma's wallpaper, despite all evidence, including the pen in its pudgy hand, proving otherwise. They will cling to Mumma's leg one moment and then escape the house to strum their penis like a banjo to impress the neighbours the next. To clarify, the toddler is banjoing their own penis, not the neighbours'. That would be a whole different book.

Next comes childhood. In the evolution of anything awesome, there is always a point at which it is a bit shit. In a human, this point is known as childhood. Children are terribly busy; they are always doing something and usually they are giving it a red-hot go but are doing it badly, which would be fine but they absolutely have to have you watch them do it. They can even make already terrible activities worse: cricket, violin, karate.

Children all have guardians whose job it is to cheer on their endeavours, creating a confidence in the child that gives a foundation sass needed to learn skills they will use for the rest of their lives: reading, writing, along with things they will never use again like Roman numerals and xylophone. The guardians that guide them are all perfect and flawed to various degrees, from occasionally right through to fundamentally. The child is designed in such a way that they are besotted with the adult no matter what.

Despite the tin-pot quality of a child, grand expectations are now placed on them. Confidence, organisation, respect for others and the need to be a unique individual are required as bare minimums in their character arsenal, even though the adults demanding these qualities have never mastered more than a couple of these simultaneously themselves.

Next up is puberty. Often maligned, the teenager is a complicated beast. If shaping up well, they should be loose cannons, ready to work hard at something they love to do, take risks and make mistakes with a softish place to land. They do all this while trying to live up to unrealistic ideals, physically and mentally, while not getting a hard-on at a picture of a medieval wench in history or bleeding on school furniture.

The disparities distributed and choices made since birth begin to strengthen or weaken the human in the teenage years. Many teenagers become disillusioned by their adults and believe them to be idiots. The more self-aware adults have known they are idiots for a while and are relieved that the cat is out of the bag. Conversely, the teenager believes they know everything while being deliciously dumb. They are still asking why a lot, but now it is in order to get things they are not responsible enough for yet, or to get out of doing the responsible jobs that would earn them some of the things they desire most.

The child that broke your or your partner's privates then slugged around to suction-cup itself to a nipple or a cheek now maintains a safe distance unless they require transport, food, shelter or finance. Now the adults are the ones asking why a lot.

The adult years have fewer typical features than the years that come before. In general though, the person will have to decide where they stand on a few key areas: health, wealth, passion, profession, family and friends. So many choices to make, also so many choices taken. Lead or follow, be frivolous or tidy, be told who you are or decide for yourself. Eat alone or get taken out. Travel or build community, stay stuck in a bad feeling or place or find a way to better it. There are infinite options in all of the realms, more than ever before, and some absolute tool started a rumour that happiness could be achieved by getting all of them in perfect balance. There is no such thing as balance, only the next right thing to do.

If you are lucky life is long and even the luckiest have to overcome adversity, so it is worth finding a way to enjoy it. Perhaps tap into your inner baby, who was deeply loved by someone or many and was more than willing to accept others' help. Perhaps remember yourself as a toddler, naked and unashamed, loving you and your little fat belly sick. Channel your inner child, the part of you that found wonder in the most mundane of new skills given best efforts. There is even something to learn from the teenager, to have the courage of your convictions and fall in love hard if it presents itself. These are all qualities we have that are best not forgotten.

Now for old age, maybe. If you have been lucky enough to outgrow cribs, highchairs and sitting cross-legged on the lino carpet, should you no longer choose to watch a film lying belly-down on carpet or slumped on a bean bag, should you instead now like to sprawl on a sofa hugging scatter cushions, you are where I am: somewhere between 24 and 80 and still alive. Well done.

Considering life and aging commences at the point of conception or at the time of birth (depending on your view of the world) and is said to end at death, then ponder that 50 per cent of the world's population will not make it from birth to even 70 years old. How do we even know what old is? If I can pinpoint my growing as a human so far through seating arrangements, then I feel I will know I am old when I can no longer sprawl on sofas and I command instead only a high-backed armchair; I shall wear it like a throne.

I have had a life and a character that has gifted me with an innate love of very nearly all humans, especially the vulnerable ones, that some people save for other creatures. I have always been a people person rather than an animal person. I will smile at the puppy on your camera roll: bringing new puppy home, puppy in the bath, puppy being a puppy, puppy in a tennis outfit, puppy wrestling a slipper (that's enough pictures now), puppy on the beach, puppy in its new bed. For the love of Lassie, please stop! I am happy for the joy you clearly feel but I get nothing from the puppy, nada.

Should we, however, be out walking and stumble across a super-old person with a little raisin head, Lego shoes and fairy-floss hair, my heart just bursts.

I will plead with my husband. 'Can we keep her? Can we *please*? I promise to take her out for walks. You know I will clean up for her. I promise I will, truly I promise.'

I imagine a future where I ruffle her behind the ears and wrestle to get the slipper out of her mouth.

Steve will say, 'I know you *say* you will look after her, darling, but you said that about the last two and just look what happened to them.'

I fear I am running out of time, but I do not fear getting old. I am quite looking forward to it. I have already picked where I shall live. Working on the district and seeing some places up close certainly limits your selection, but it assures you there are great places too. The husband and I will be going in a lifestyle village. It is a gated community for the elderly, like Jurassic Park for old people. My husband can busy himself growling at anyone that drives over the 5km/hr limit within the complex and emptying the dishwasher, and I can busy myself in the pool with aqua aerobics (and water jets). I shall join line dancing and keep an eye on my neighbours, so I have something to add to conversation on coffee club Tuesdays. The neighbours will tell me things because 'she used to be a nurse, you know'. I shall never run for club president, only megalomaniacs wish for that kind of power, but I shall help the committee decorate the community hall for Christmas and Saint Patrick's Day celebrations, and even Australia Day, if they change the date.

Should I die before Steve, I will know I was loved and that he will be a short and pragmatic griever, thank goodness. The children shall remember me as either inspirational or flakey and that is for them to decide. They would have evidence to back either perception. Should my Steve die before I do, through salmon-deficiency disorder perhaps, I shall have a community around me with which to busy myself. I will get out Nat's tablemat and watch *Heartbeat* re-runs. I am sure they will still be a thing. Will that program ever die? Should my children have full lives outside of me, I will count it as a blessing and explain that when they visit they must take me out, to the zoo and some wineries, perhaps as there is only room for one at my table. I will borrow little grandchildren from around the village if I have none of my own. I will not even have to ask; they will just come flocking. I will have Hot Wheel cars in a box in the corner of my lounge and an unrivalled biscuit cupboard. I will be like the Pied Piper, but with excellent intentions.

I will have my narcotics-spiked ice-cube tray for special occasions and perhaps a spare one for friends if I have freezer space. I shall document with the GP my medical wishes because I am frightened medicine can sometimes do more than it should. I shall have some trout in the freezer too just in case they do not listen, and I am ready to go by anaphylaxis before 'whoever' is ready to take me. I have no regrets at this point but there is still time. I shall carry a water pistol loaded with blue ink at all times to squirt at anyone trying to resuscitate me against my wishes. I shall say a quick prayer before I die just in case the Lord is real and if he is, I shall apologise to him for taking his son on that dreadful road trip around South Australia and for Mum's sloppiness making us lose Jesus for a short while in Mount Gambier.

# TWENTY-THREE

# THE MORGUE

## WHERE'S THE GATORADE BOTTLE? SURELY IT'S HERE SOMEWHERE?

Given everything that you have read in this book, please know that it is a miracle you are alive. It is a miracle to me that you bought my book, and I am grateful that you did.

I hope you enjoyed reading it as much as I enjoyed writing it. It may have hurt a little sometimes. Hopefully, it made you piss your pants too. If it did, please be sure to tell your friends on your socials. Let them know it was Nurse Georgie who broke you. They may even offer to come around and help freshen you up. (See instructions on page 218.)

One more small favour, too, could you just go check if they do these shrouds in a different colour? This yellow one makes me look really pale. I would get it myself but I can't get the zip open from inside the body bag.

It is not customary to put more dedications at the end, but it's my book and I suppose why not?

I cannot personally thank every nurse that has taught me something, picked me up or made me laugh, so let us bring it back to thanking one nurse that represents all of them.

Thank you, from the bottom of my heart thank you, to the nurse that held Granny Whitworth's hand as she passed. This book is dedicated to you and all those like you going the extra mile for all of us.

Love from Nurse Georgie